ASSESSMENT PACK
with Audio CD and Test Generating CD-ROM

5
FOCUS
ON
GRAMMAR
AN INTEGRATED SKILLS APPROACH

THIRD EDITION

JOAN JAMIESON
CAROL A. CHAPELLE

WITH
LESLIE GRANT
BETHANY GRAY
XIANGYING JIANG
HSIN-MIN LIU
KEVIN ZIMMERMAN

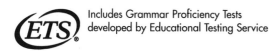

Includes Grammar Proficiency Tests
developed by Educational Testing Service

PEARSON
Longman

Focus on Grammar 5: An Integrated Skills Course   Assessment Pack

Pearson Education, 10 Bank Street, White Plains, NY 10606

Staff credits: The people who made up the *Focus on Grammar 5: An Integrated Skills Course, Assessment Pack* team, representing editorial, production, design, and manufacturing, are listed below:

Rhea Banker
Nancy Blodgett
Elisabeth Carlson
Christine Edmonds
Margot Gramer
Stacey Hunter
Laura Le Dréan
Wendy Long
Michael Mone
Linda Moser
Julie Schmidt

ISBN: 0-13-193138-5

LONGMAN ON THE **WEB**

Longman.com offers online resources for teachers and students. Access our Companion Websites, our online catalog, and our local offices around the world.

Visit us at **longman.com**.

Printed in the United States of America
3 4 5 6 7 8 9 10—BAH—10 09 08 07

Contents

Introduction

The *Focus on Grammar 5 Assessment Pack* includes the following assessment tools to help you determine students' grammar proficiency level and monitor their progress and achievement in the *Focus on Grammar* course.

In addition to the tools listed below, a separately packaged *Focus on Grammar Placement Test* (ISBN 0-13-199437-9) is also available. To obtain a copy of the *Placement Test,* contact your local Longman ELT specialist.

FOG Student Book Assessment Tools

- Part Diagnostic and Achievement Tests
- Unit Achievement Tests
- Audio CD with the listening portions of the Diagnostic and Achievement Tests

Supplementary Assessment Tools

- Two ETS Grammar Proficiency Tests (Levels 4 and 5)
- Test-Generating CD-ROM

You can find detailed descriptions of each type of assessment tool, as well as instructions on administering and scoring the tests, in the "General Information" sections that precede the test forms.

About the Authors

Joan Jamieson, Project Director, is a Professor in the Applied Linguistics program in the English Department at Northern Arizona University. She received her Ph.D. from the University of Illinois at Urbana-Champaign. Dr. Jamieson is the author of several publications on English as a Second Language assessment and computer-assisted language learning. She has collaborated with Pearson Longman and Carol Chapelle in the past on several projects, including *Longman English Assessment* and the testing program for *Longman English Interactive.*

Carol A. Chapelle, Project Director, is a Professor of TESL/Applied Linguistics at Iowa State University. She received her Ph.D. from the University of Illinois at Urbana-Champaign. She is the author of *Computer applications in second language acquisition: Foundations for teaching, testing and research* (Cambridge University Press, 2001), *English language learning and technology: Lectures on teaching and research in the age of information and communication technology.* (John Benjamins Publishing, 2003), and *ESOL tests and testing: A resource for teachers and program administrators* (TESOL Publications, 2005). Dr. Chapelle was until recently the editor of *TESOL Quarterly.* She has collaborated with Joan Jamieson and Pearson Longman in the past on several projects, including *Longman English Assessment* and the testing program for *Longman English Interactive.*

Project Staff

The following people worked on the development of the tests under the guidance of Joan Jamieson and Carol Chapelle:

Leslie Grant, Ph.D., Northern Arizona University

Bethany Gray, MA-TESL student, Iowa State University

Xiangying Jiang, Ph.D. student, Northern Arizona University

Hsin-min Liu, MA-TESL, Iowa State University

Kevin Zimmerman, MA-TESL, Brigham Young University

and

Liza Armstrong, MA-TESL, Northern Arizona University

Maja Grgurovic, Ph.D. student, Iowa State University

James McCormick, Ph.D., Michigan State University

Erin Kate Murphy, MA-TESL, Northern Arizona University

Pamela Pearson, MA-TESL student, Iowa State University

Lia Plakans, Ph.D. student, University of Iowa

Kornwipa Poonpon, Ph.D. student, Northern Arizona University

Kerri Quinn, MA-TESL, Northern Arizona University

Betsy Tremmel, MA student, Iowa State University

Part Diagnostic Tests, Unit Achievement Tests, and Part Achievement Tests

General Information

Overview

The *Focus on Grammar* Part Diagnostic, Unit Achievement, and Part Achievement Tests have set a new standard in ELT grammar teaching and testing. Developed under the direction of applied linguists Joan Jamieson and Carol A. Chapelle, these tests

- are manageable in length and easy to administer and score;
- accurately reflect the material presented in the Grammar in Context, Grammar Charts and Notes, and Focused Practice sections of the course;
- offer a sufficient number of items to assess students' knowledge of each grammar point;
- include a wide variety of item types;
- provide a powerful remediation tool.

About the Test Development

These tests have been carefully developed so that the weighting and distribution of test items mirror those of the Student Book content. For example, if 40 percent of the items in a unit practice the simple present and 60 percent of the items practice the present progressive, then the Unit Achievement Test maintains the same balance. The Part Diagnostic and Achievement Tests additionally reflect the distribution of items across the units in a part. For example, if one unit in a part has 110 practice items, and the second unit in the part has 53 practice items, then the Part Diagnostic and Achievement Tests maintain the same balance.

Using the Tests for Remediation Purposes

Codes provided in the Answer Key help you determine what grammar points students might be having difficulty with. In the Unit Achievement tests, each answer has a code that refers to one or more of the Grammar Notes or to the Grammar Chart. In the Part Diagnostic and Part Achievement tests, each answer has a code that refers to the unit where the item was presented. By referring to these codes, both you and the student can try to pinpoint grammar points that are causing confusion or proving to be difficult.

EXAMPLE:

Item 5 in Exercise 3 of the Unit 15 Achievement Test has the code **N2**. This means that the item is testing the grammar point associated with Grammar Note 2 in the student book: "Many verbs and verb phrases in English have gerunds as objects. Common examples: *avoid, consider, enjoy, keep, mind.* We often use *go* + gerund to talk about recreational activities: *go skiing, go swimming, go hiking,* etc." If a student answered this item incorrectly, that student may need more help with this grammar point.

NOTE: If a test item has two codes separated by a comma (for example, `N1, N2` or `U1, U2`), that item is testing two grammar points or two units.

Test Purpose and Design

The **Part Diagnostic Tests** help you determine how well students know the material they are about to study in the next part of the Student Book. Since the material they are about to study is usually new, students often score low on these tests. If students score high on a Part Diagnostic Test, you may want to review the results to tailor instruction. You may determine, for example, that you do not need to teach all of the material in that part.

Each Part Diagnostic Test takes 50 minutes and includes about 60 items. The test begins with a listening exercise, includes several contextualized grammar exercises, and ends with an editing exercise.

The **Unit Achievement Tests** help you assess students' knowledge of the specific grammatical topics presented in the unit. If students have mastered the material presented in the unit, they should answer most of the questions correctly. The codes provided in the Answer Key help you determine what grammar topics students may need to review.

Each Unit Achievement Test takes 30 minutes and includes about 30 items. The test begins with a listening exercise, includes two to three contextualized grammar exercises, and ends with an editing exercise.

The **Part Achievement Tests** help you determine how well students have mastered the material they have studied in that part of the student book. If students have mastered the material presented in the part, they should answer most of the questions correctly. The codes provided in the Answer Key help you determine what units students may need to review.

Each Part Achievement Test is identical in structure to the Part Diagnostic Test for the part, including the same number of items and testing the same grammar points with equal balance and weighting. By comparing a student's results on the Part Diagnostic Test and on the Part Achievement Test, you can determine how much students have learned. A high score on the Part Achievement Test indicates improvement. Note, however, that if students scored high on the Part Diagnostic Test, you may not be able to detect any improvement on the Part Achievement Test.

Administering the Tests

Before administering a test:

- Make photocopies of the test form.
- Set up your CD player in the testing room and check the volume.
- Check the track list on the inside back cover for which track you will need to play.

The listening section in the Part Diagnostic, Unit Achievement, and Part Achievement Tests is the first section of the test so that it may be administered to all students at the same time without interfering with the other parts of the test. When students are ready to begin the test, play the audio CD and have students listen and answer the questions. You should play each track two times.

After students have completed the listening section, stop the CD and ask students to work on the remaining sections of the test.

Scoring the Tests

To determine a student's score on the tests, add up the number of questions the student answered correctly, using the Answer Key on pages 195–222. You may also wish to subtract the number incorrect from the total number of items. The total number of items for each test is shown on the first page of the test.

To determine the percentage score, first divide the number correct by the total number of items; then, multiply that proportion by 100. (Use the total number of items on the test, not the number of items that a student answered.)

EXAMPLE:

The Part VI Achievement Test includes 60 items.
A student answered 47 items correctly.

$47 \div 60 = .78 \rightarrow .78 \times 100 = 78$

The student's percentage score is 78%.

A scoring box is provided on the first page of each test to record the student's score.

PART I Diagnostic Test

60 Items
Score:_____

1 | LISTENING: NEW ALBUM REVIEW

🎧 **A.** *Listen to this album review on the radio. Complete the review by writing the word(s) that you hear. You will hear the recording two times.*

Erin Henderson _____*has been creating*_____ music since she was five. Although her name
           0.

may be unfamiliar to you, people around the world _____ her voice. She
           1.

has released seven albums, and she is preparing to release her eighth album, *Family of Man*, this

week. Her unique style _____ combines elements of African and
          2.

European music. She began recording her new album in a studio, but in the end, she recorded

most of the songs in an empty swimming pool. As you _____ to the
          3.

album, you _____ birds in the background, and, in one song, a plane is
      4.

flying overhead. Some of the songs _____ you dance, while others
          5.

_____ you.
    6.

Before she started work on *Family of Man*, Henderson had taken some time off from

songwriting to travel to the Far East. Her travels have influenced her music for the better. As you

_____ to *Family of Man*, you _____ how many
    7.   **8.**

changes she has made in her style. She used to rely _____ on
          9.

instrumentation in her music. Now, she _____ fewer instruments, which
          10.

focuses the listener on her voice. I believe this is her finest work yet.

B. *Reread the album review. Then read each statement and circle* **T** *(true) or* **F** *(false). The first answer is already given.*

Ⓣ **F**   **0.** Henderson started creating music when she was young, and she continues to write music today.

T **F**   **1.** Henderson released her first album some time ago, but she continues to record new albums.

T **F**   **2.** Henderson has released her most recent album already.

T **F**   **3.** Henderson started recording her songs in a studio before changing to an empty swimming pool.

T **F**   **4.** Henderson started work on *Family of Man*. Then she traveled to the Far East.

T **F**   **5.** In the past, travels inspired Henderson to compose music, but they don't now.

T **F**   **6.** Henderson relied more on instrumentation in the past than she does now.

C. *Reread the album review. Find three action verbs and three non-action verbs. Write them in the table below. An example is given.*

ACTION VERBS	NON-ACTION VERBS
has released	
1. _____	1. _____
2. _____	2. _____
3. _____	3. _____

2 | WHERE'S THE NEW MUSIC?

A. *Read this e-mail to the radio station that broadcast the review about Henderson's new album. Complete the e-mail by writing the correct verbs from the box.*

had been buying	had heard	haven't heard
was going	~~bought~~	aren't playing
have been listening	isn't listening	used to

To Whom It May Concern:

I want to thank you for broadcasting that review of Erin Henderson's new album, *Family of Man*. I _____ bought _____ her album after I _____ your
0.   **1.**
review (it was hard to find the album), and I love it! I remember that my roommate

_____ listen to her, and I enjoyed the music, but I never knew who was
2.
singing. Also, I'm writing because I _____ closely to your station every
3.
day at work, but I _____ you play any of the songs from her new album
4.
yet. I _____ to tell all my friends to listen to your station so that they
5.
could hear her. I wonder why you _____ her music. What's going on?
6.
Debby

B. *Reread the e-mail. Find three action verbs and three non-action verbs. Write them in the table below. An example is given.*

ACTION VERBS	NON-ACTION VERBS
1. _____	O. *want* _____
2. _____	1. _____
3. _____	2. _____
	3. _____

3 | THE PRODUCER'S RESPONSE

Read this radio producer's reply to Debby's e-mail. Complete the reply by writing the correct forms of the verbs in the blanks.

Dear Debby,

Thank you for writing to us about Henderson's new album. We often

_____*receive*_____ e-mail from music fans, but we were very surprised by the
        0. (receive)

response we _____ when we _____ the review of
                    1. (get)   **2. (play)**

Henderson's new album! We _____ to receive her CD for several weeks
                                    3. (expect)

now, but we still _____ it. In fact, we _____ to
                        4. (not / receive)   **5. (plan)**

play her album immediately after we broadcast the review. It wasn't until our staff member

reached for the CD at the end of the review that he _____ that it
                                                            6. (realize)

_____ yet. After calling the record company, we found out that there had
    7. (not / come in)

been a shipping mistake.

We _____ to receive the CD soon. We _____ you for your
        8. (hope)   **9. (thank)**

interest, and we hope that you _____ to listen to our station.
                                        10. (continue)

Sincerely yours,

Robin Warner, Producer

4 | EDITING: WORD OF MOUTH

Read the conversation between Debby and her friend, Ben, about her new Henderson album. There are 17 mistakes in the use of verbs. The first mistake is already corrected. Find and correct 16 more.

BEN: What ~~do~~ *are* you ~~listen~~ *listening* to?

DEBBY: Erin Henderson. I had bought her album yesterday, and I was listening to it ever since.

BEN: She is sounding great. Where do you hear about her?

DEBBY: I had worked when I was hearing a review of this album. I actually would have a

roommate who use to listen to her all the time. She would own all her albums, and she

sings along. I was liking her music then, but I am loving it now! The reviewer said that

she was traveling in the Far East before she recorded this album and that her style has

really improve because of her experiences there. Her music isn't sounding Asian now, or

anything, but she had just matured as a singer and songwriter.

Unit 1 Achievement Test

30 Items
Score: _____

---

1 | LISTENING: TRAVEL AD

🎧 *Listen to this radio ad for a travel agency. Complete the ad by writing the word(s) that you hear. You will hear the recording two times.*

It's early in the morning in the heart of the Amazonian rain forest. Toucans

_____*are calling*_____ to each other. Monkeys _____ in the
        0.   **1.**

trees. A tourist _____ down an overgrown trail, stopping from time to
                  2.

time to take in the exotic sights and sounds of the jungle.

Do you _____ that tourist was you? Well, imagine that your dream
              3.

has come true. You _____ a ticket for the Amazon Adventure Tour. Look
                4.

at your exciting itinerary! You _____ in Manaus, Brazil, at 10 A.M. on
                   5.

Sunday, and you _____ at your luxurious hotel overlooking the Amazon
              6.

River at 1:00 P.M. As soon as you check in, you _____ to relax. During
                    7.

your week-long stay at the hotel, you _____ the time of your life! With
                  8.

river cruises and trips to local villages on the itinerary, by the end of your vacation, you

_____ the magic of the Amazon!
         9.

My name is Donna, and I'm a travel agent. Whether your dream destination is the

Amazon or some other exotic locale, I'll work with you to plan the perfect vacation! I

_____ people like you to plan their dream vacations for more than 20
        10.

years, so call me today!

---

2 | AT THE TRAVEL AGENCY

Read this conversation at the travel agency. Then read each statement and circle **T** *(true) or* **F** *(false).*

CHRIS: I heard your ad on the radio, and I want some help planning a trip to Rio de Janeiro.

DONNA: Oh! I've been to Rio four times. It's a great city! Will you be traveling for Carnival?

CHRIS: Yes. I've been wanting to see Carnival there for a long time, and I really need a vacation, so I'm taking some time off in February.

DONNA: You're going to love it! Listen, Chris, I've put together a Rio vacation package that I think you'll be interested in. Let me tell you about it.

T **Ⓕ** **0.** Someone helped Chris to plan his trip already.

T **F** **1.** Chris is going to travel to Carnival this year.

T **F** **2.** Chris wanted to see Carnival in the past, and he still wants to see it.

T **F** **3.** Chris went on vacation recently.

T **F** **4.** Chris plans to take a vacation in February.

T **F** **5.** Donna is sure that Chris will love Carnival.

T **F** **6.** Donna had a Rio vacation package in the past, but she doesn't have one now.

3 | RIO ITINERARY

Read this conversation about the itinerary for the Rio vacation package. Complete the conversation by writing verb forms from the box.

leave	'll be seeing	has been	'll be sightseeing
sounds	'll have seen	~~arrive~~	'll have

DONNA: Here's what's included in the Rio vacation package: You _____*arrive*_____

                        0.

    in Brazil on Wednesday, February 2nd, and you _____ the

                                                1.

    following Wednesday, February 9th.

CHRIS: I _____ access to all the local Carnival parades, won't I?

                        2.

DONNA: Yes, of course! There are also going to be opportunities for you to visit places

    like Ipanema Beach, Copacabana, Petropolis, and Sugar Loaf.

    You _____ during the day and dancing to samba music at

                   3.

    night! By the end of your trip, you _____ not only Carnival,

                                         4.

    but also many of the other wonderful sights in Rio.

CHRIS: This vacation _____ wonderful! I'm ready to leave today!

                           5.

4 | EDITING: INVITATION TO A FRIEND

Read Chris's e-mail to a friend. There are ten mistakes in the use of the simple present, present progressive, present perfect, present perfect progressive, simple future, and future perfect progressive. The first mistake is already corrected. Find and correct nine more.

Dear Rob,

    I ~~will have~~ *have* some big news! I tell you before that I will want to take a vacation, right? Well, you'll never believe it, but I'm going to Brazil in February for Carnival! By then, I'll be working for almost three years without a vacation. I'll be reading some information about Carnival and Rio on the Internet, and it sounds amazing! I'll be planning to stay there for a week. I stay in a hotel by the ocean, and I visit all the sights! I'll be wondering if you want to go with me. I'm going to buy my tickets already, but my travel agent says there's room in the hotel and on the plane if you want to go.

Let me know,

Chris

Unit 2 Achievement Test

1 | LISTENING: A PUBLIC PROPOSAL

🎧 **A.** *Listen to this local news report about a public marriage proposal. Complete the report by writing the word(s) that you hear. You will hear the recording two times.*

Jim Reed first _____ met _____ his wife, Nancy, on a stage while hundreds of
0.

people were watching. Jim _____ in a rock-and-roll band. Nancy, a local
1.

artist, liked Jim and had been going to his shows regularly. Then one night, the drummer didn't

show up. After Jim had sung a couple of songs without the drummer, he jokingly asked the

audience if anyone wanted to come up and play the drums for the rest of the show. Nancy

_____ how to play the drums, but she _____
2. **3.**

pass up the opportunity to meet Jim. So she volunteered to play and took a seat behind the

drums. The noise she made wasn't pretty. Fortunately, she had only played for a couple of

minutes when the real drummer arrived. It turned out that Jim liked Nancy, even though she was

a terrible drummer. After they had dated for a few months, Jim decided to propose the same way

they had met—in front of a large audience. Jim had it all planned: He

_____ ask Nancy to come on stage, then he would propose to her.
4.

However, Nancy had heard ahead of time what Jim _____ to do, so
5.

while Jim was still outside, she told the audience and gave them confetti. When Jim proposed to

Nancy, the audience surprised him with the confetti! Jim and Nancy were married later that year.

B. *Reread the local news report. Then read each statement and circle* **T** *(true) or* **F** *(false).*

T   **F**   **0.** Jim first met Nancy on stage before he sang songs.

T   Ⓕ   **1.** Jim always asked the audience to play drums before he sang songs.

T   **F**   **2.** Nancy had only seen Jim perform once before she met him.

T   **F**   **3.** Jim sang in a rock-and-roll band in the past, and he still sings in one today.

T   **F**   **4.** Jim thought he would ask Nancy to marry him on stage.

T   **F**   **5.** Nancy planned a surprise with the audience before Jim proposed to her.

2 | TWO MAYORS, ONE WEDDING

A. *Julie and Paul, mayors of two neighboring Minnesota towns, tell a local newspaper reporter the story of how they first met. Complete the conversation by writing the correct forms of the verbs in the blanks. Use simple past and past perfect.*

REPORTER: When _____*did*_____ you two first _____*meet*_____ ?
                           0. (meet)

JULIE: I _____ Paul years ago. He was working in the mailroom in City Hall,
              1. (meet)

and I was working as a court recorder. We used to chat in the lunchroom, and I

would always bring him cookies. We kind of liked each other, but I found out that he

was going to move to Washington, D.C. to pursue his political career. That made me

feel like we had no future because someone had just offered me a new job here, and I

_____ to accept it. Besides, he was a Republican and I was a
        2. (decide)

Democrat!

REPORTER: So how did you finally end up together?

PAUL: Well, I did go to Washington, D.C., but I soon realized that I could serve people

better here at home. So I _____ back in 2000. Julie and I had stayed in
                                       3. (come)

touch over the years, and we had both become quite involved in public service. When

the elections for mayor came up, Julie and I were talking on the phone almost every

day to give each other advice. I wanted to help her, especially because I

_____ more campaign experience than she had. And Julie helped me
        4. (have)

with the local issues because she had become much more knowledgeable about them

than I was. I _____ shortly after we were both elected.
                      5. (propose)

B. *Reread the conversation. Find two past progressive verbs and two habitual past event verbs. Write them in the table below. An example is given.*

PAST PROGRESSIVE	HABITUAL PAST EVENT
was working	
1. _____	1. _____
2. _____	2. _____

3 │ EDITING: JIM AND NANCY, TWO YEARS LATER

Read this local newspaper article. There are 12 mistakes in the use of the present perfect, simple past, past progressive, past perfect, and **used to**. *The first mistake is already corrected. Find and correct 11 more. (Note: There can be more than one way to correct a mistake.)*

                                                                     was . . . going

Two years after they were married, Jim and Nancy's marriage ~~had~~ still ~~gone~~ strong. When telephoned last month, Jim has quitted his band and has finished his degree in accounting. Although Jim hadn't sung in the band anymore, he said, "I've always believed that music was bringing us together, and we still share that." Nancy also changed careers. She used to work as an artist when she met Jim, but she has switched to teaching art at a high school shortly after they got married. She said, "I would think about how cool we were, me an artist and Jim a rock singer. I did dream that we would be famous. Soon it became obvious, however, that we just haven't made enough money, so we had to change careers. I guess we had both matured a little bit."

Unit 3 Achievement Test

| 30 Items |
| Score: _____ |

1 | LISTENING: NEGATIVE EFFECTS OF TV

∩ **A.** *Listen to this student read his essay about television. Complete the essay by writing the word(s) that you hear. You will hear the recording two times.*

When I was little, I _____*watched*_____ hours of television every day. Unfortunately, the time
       0.

that I _____ sitting in front of the television could have been put to better use by
              1.

playing outside or learning a skill.

I believe that watching television has harmful effects on a person's health and mind. First of

all, television _____ affects people's health. We all know that exercise is good for
                    2.

our health. However, many people _____ to sit and eat junk food while watching
                                       3.

TV. If you do this for many years, the lack of activity will probably begin to make you feel bad.

You probably won't have much energy, and you might gain weight.

In addition, _____ is research that shows that people who watch TV for many
                4.

hours per day have lower IQs than people who read.

To conclude, if you care about your physical and mental health, _____ your
                                                                        5.

TV!

B. *Reread the essay. Then read each statement and circle* **T** *(true) or* **F** *(false).*

T **Ⓕ** 0. This student watched very little TV.

T **F** 1. This student thinks that television has bad effects on people's minds.

T **F** 2. People understand that they will be healthy if they exercise.

T **F** 3. If you like to sit and eat junk food while watching TV, you'll have energy.

T **F** 4. People should pay attention to IQ research comparing people who watch TV
for many hours per day and people who read.

T **F** 5. People who read have lower IQs than people who watch TV many hours each
day.

2 | BENEFITS OF TV

Read this student's essay about television. Write the letter of the best answer on each line.

I ___d___ (**a. believes b. recognizes c. stop d. think**) that television can _____ (**a. benefit b. give**
0.   1.

c. keeps d. has) people. Many people _____ (**a. has b. gives c. feel d. keep**) that there are many
2.

wonderful programs on television. For instance, public television _____ (**a. stop b. has c. is**
3.

loving d. is feeling) a wide selection of educational shows for children. Not only do kids _____
4.

(**a. thinks b. give c. recognizes d. love**) and watch these shows every day, but parents appreciate them

because they _____ (**a. entertains b. have c. know d. learns**) that their kids are learning as they
5.

watch. They often _____ (**a. show b. stop c. are liking d. are having**) their support for these
6.

programs by sending money to help pay for them. For adults, there are many shows that both

educate and _____ (**a. entertain b. considers c. keep d. learns**). In addition, television _____
7.   8.

(**a. entertain b. stops c. know d. keeps**) people informed about current events in the world around

them.

For these reasons, I _____ (**a. am liking b. am giving c. consider d. recognizes**) television to be
9.

beneficial. With careful programming, both children and adults can _____ (**a. have b. stop**
10.

c. thinks d. learn) from television, instead of being harmed by it.

3 | TECHNOLOGY EXHIBIT

Read this phone conversation between Jeff and Adam. Complete the conversation by writing the correct forms of the verbs in the blanks. Use the simple or the progressive form.

YUJI: Hey, Adam. I wanted to know if you'd like to go to the technology exhibit downtown.

They ___*are showing*___ all kinds of neat new technology products.
0. (show)

ADAM: I'd really like to go, but I can't. A repairman _____ my television right
1. (fix)

now. It hasn't been working all week. Plus, I _____ some trouble with my
2. (have)

printer. It _____ anything right now.
3. (not / print)

YUJI: Oh no! Well, I _____ it's not the best time for you to go to a show like
4. (guess)

this right now.

ADAM: You're right. You know, I _____ all my electronic gadgets, but not when
5. (love)

they're broken!

4 | EDITING: HEALTH EXHIBIT

Read another telephone conversation between Yuji and Adam. There are six mistakes in the use of action and non-action verbs. The first mistake is already corrected. Find and correct five more.

YUJI: Hey, Adam. You don't sound very ~~well~~ good. Are you sick?

ADAM: Yeah, I feel terribly.

YUJI: That's too bad. I'm call because there're another exhibit downtown called Advancing

Healthcare Technology. It looks interesting. Do you want to go?

ADAM: I think I'd better stay home and try to sleep.

YUJI: OK. Sleep good, and I'm hoping you'll feel better soon!

Part I Achievement Test

60 Items
Score: _____

🎧 **A.** *Listen to this movie review on the radio. Complete the review by writing the word(s) that you hear. You will hear the recording two times.*

Sean Collins _____*has been acting*_____ in movies since he was 12. Although his name
0.

may be unfamiliar to you, people around the world _____ his face.
1.

He has appeared in seven movies and is working on his eighth film, *Homeless*. His unique

acting style _____ combines the characteristics of a tough gangster
2.

with those of a sensitive lover. He started his acting career on Broadway as a child, but since

then he has done more acting in Hollywood. As you _____ him,
3.

you _____ a greater depth to his acting than he showed in his earlier
4.

films. Fans are betting that this film will earn him an Academy Award. Some of the scenes

_____ you breathless, while others _____ you.
5.   **6.**

Before he began work on *Homeless*, Collins had spent some time at home with his wife and

his new baby. His time off has changed him for the better. As you _____
7.

Homeless, you _____ the changes that have occurred in his acting style.
8.

He used to use _____ his voice and grand gestures. Now, he
9.

_____ with fewer gestures; instead, he relies on subtle facial expressions
10.

to reveal his character's emotions. I think this is his finest film yet.

B. *Reread the movie review. Then read each statement and circle **T** (true) or **F** (false).*

Ⓣ F   **0.** Collins started acting in the past, and he is still acting.

T   F   1. Collins acted in seven movies in the past.

T   F   2. Collins has not started to work on *Homeless*.

T   F   3. Collins first started his career on Broadway before moving to Hollywood.

T   F   4. Collins started work on *Homeless*. Then he spent time with his family.

T   F   5. Collins' acting style is the same as it was in the past.

T   F   6. Collins used gestures more in the past than he does now.

C. *Reread the movie review. Find three action verbs and three non-action verbs. Write them in the table below. An example is given.*

ACTION VERBS	NON-ACTION VERBS
O. *has been acting*	1. _____
1. _____	2. _____
2. _____	3. _____
3. _____	

| 2 | WHEN'S THE MOVIE PLAYING? |

A. *Read this e-mail to the radio station that broadcast the review about Collins' new film. Complete the e-mail by writing the correct verbs from the box.*

will be showing	hoped	used to
was going to	~~rented~~	liked
have been checking	had shown	had listened

To Whom It May Concern:

   I enjoyed listening to your recent review of Sean Collins' new film, *Homeless*. I

_____*rented*_____ a couple of his older films after I _____
          0.   **1.**
to your review, and I think he's great! I remember that my roommate

_____ own one of his movies, and I _____ it,
          2.   **3.**
but I never knew who the star was. Anyway, I hope you can answer a question: I

_____ the newspaper carefully, but I haven't seen when his film will be
          4.
coming to town. I _____ recommend that all my friends go see it. Do
                                          5.
you know when the movie _____?
                                                              6.
Jamie

B. *Reread the e-mail. Find three action verbs and three non-action verbs. Write them in the table below. An example is given.*

ACTION VERBS	NON-ACTION VERBS
1. _____	0. *enjoyed* _____
2. _____	1. _____
3. _____	2. _____
	3. _____

---

3 │ THE RADIO STATION'S RESPONSE

Read the radio producer's reply to Jamie's e-mail. Complete the reply by writing the correct forms of the verbs in the blanks.

Dear Jamie,

    Thank you for the e-mail that you _____*sent*_____ a few days ago. We
           0. (send)
were pleased by the response we _____ when we
           1. (get)
_____ the review of Sean Collins' new film. We do
    2. (air)
_____ that the movie _____ for the first
    3. (know)   **4. (show)**
time on Friday night at the local theater downtown.

    We delayed in providing this information because we _____ for
                5. (wait)
some promotional tickets for the past few days, but we _____ them
                6. (not / receive)
yet. We _____ a contest for our listeners, but the tickets
    7. (be going to hold)
_____ in time.
    8. (not / arrive)
    We _____ the delay in advertising the movie information, but we
           9. (regret)
_____ you enjoy Collins' latest movie!
    10. (hope)

Sincerely yours,

Tricia Wong, Producer

4 | EDITING: WATCHING A MOVIE

Read the conversation between Jamie and her roommate, Liz, about the DVD Homeless.
There are 17 mistakes in the use of verbs. The first mistake is already corrected. Find and correct 16 more.

LIZ: What ~~you are watching~~ *are you watching*?

JAMIE: *Homeless.* I had bought it yesterday. I was wanting the DVD ever since the movie came out.

LIZ: It is looking great. How do you find out about it?

JAMIE: I had driven and was listening to the radio when someone do a review of the movie on the radio. I actually would live with a girl who use to watch movies with Sean Collins all the time. She would own all his videos. Whenever she watched the shows, she says all his lines. I was enjoying his acting then, but now I'm thinking he's the best! The reviewer said that before Collins started work on this last movie, he was staying at home with his son for a few months and that his acting has really changed after that. These days, he isn't really looking any different, but he had definitely improved as an actor.

PART II Diagnostic Test

1 | LISTENING: WORK OF ART

🎧 **A.** *Doug and Liza are visiting an art museum. Listen and complete their conversation by writing the word(s) that you hear. You will hear the recording two times.*

DOUG: That's an amazing painting, _____*isn't it*_____ ?
0.

LIZA: It is amazing! The artist _____ worked on it for years. You
1.

_____ get a picture of it!
2.

DOUG: We _____ take pictures of the paintings. But we
3.

_____ look in the gift shop when we're done. They might have
4.

a print of this painting. Most museums _____ sell prints of
5.

their most popular paintings. At least the museums that I've been to do. Look at the

date of the painting. When you first looked at it, you _____
6.

thought it was painted from a photograph. I know I did. But it

_____ . It was painted before the camera was invented.
7.

Incredible, _____ ?
8.

LIZA: It is! What kind of paint do you think he used? It _____
9.

regular oil paint. I've never seen anything like it.

DOUG: _____ I. And I even studied art like this in college.
10.

LIZA: So _____ I! You know, I'm afraid we may not be able to find a
11.

print in the gift shop. Maybe we could take a picture after all. We

_____ take the picture with the flash. Do you think we could?
12.

DOUG: We _____ . We might get into trouble.
13.

B. *Reread the conversation. Then read each statement and circle **T** (true) or **F** (false).*

(T) **F** 0. Liza agrees that the painting is amazing.

T F 1. Liza is absolutely certain that the artist spent years working on the painting.

T F 2. It is OK for visitors to take one or two pictures of paintings at the museum.

T F 3. Doug doesn't think that the painting is incredible, but Liza does.

T F 4. Doug has never seen the kind of paint used in the painting.

T F 5. Doug thought the painting was painted from a photograph, and it was.

T F 6. The museums that Doug has been to sell prints of their popular paintings.

T F 7. Both Doug and Liza studied art.

T F 8. Liza is not certain that she can find a print at the gift shop.

T F 9. Doug thinks Lisa shouldn't take a picture because they might get into trouble.

T F 10. Doug is certain that the gift shop has a print of the painting.

2 | HOW TO APPRECIATE ART

A. *Read this museum pamphlet about art appreciation. Complete the pamphlet. Use the items from the box. Choose the most appropriate item for each blank. Use items only once.*

ought to	might have been	must have been	should
are not given	were to	could have	so can
're not supposed to	must not	don't	~~do you~~
doesn't have to	couldn't have been		

Some people simply don't appreciate art. ____*Do you*____? You may not now,
                                                    0.

but that's OK. Many people _____. However, you can learn to
                                       1.

appreciate art. Here are three suggestions:

First, you _____ rush through art museums. Take your time. You
                    2.

might consider studying the artwork up close, then from far away. Try to think about what the

artist _____ thinking when creating the piece.
              3.

Second, you _____ talk about art with someone else. The other
                     4.

person _____ be knowledgeable about art—in fact, a knowledgeable
              5.

person might make you feel afraid to give your opinion. You must not be afraid to simply talk

about how the artwork makes you feel.

Third, you _____ learn something about the artists and their times.
                       6.

For instance, you may see an abstract painting and think that the artist

_____ insane, but you _____ judge artists'
            7.   **8.**

personal lives by their paintings. Some abstract artists _____ more
                                                                        9.

normal!

If you remember to do these three things, you might just gain a greater appreciation of art.

Then, when other people are talking about a great work of art, _____
                                                                              10.

you.

B. *Reread the museum pamphlet. Then read each statement and circle the correct word(s).*

0. There are many people who (know / (don't know)) how to appreciate art.

1. It (is / is not) OK to rush through art museums.

2. It (is / is not) suggested that people only study artwork from far away.

3. It (is / is not) a good idea to talk about art with someone else who has not studied art.

4. People who want to learn to appreciate art (should / should not) be afraid of talking about it.

5. We (might / might not) think that abstract artists are normal, but many are.

3 | MUSEUM SUFFERS FINANCIAL CRISIS

*Read this newspaper article about the future of the local art museum. Complete the article by writing the correct forms of the modals, modal-like expressions, **be** verbs, or auxiliaries in the blanks.*

The City Art Museum _____*might be closing*_____ its doors by the end of the
                              0. (might / close)

year, according to museum director Marty Hall, if visits by patrons do not increase. Hall isn't

sure they will.

A city law states that the museum _____ remain open if it
                                          1. (not / allow)

is losing money, which it _____. Many people argue that
                                   2. (be)

the law _____ four years ago, but it
              3. (should / not / be passed)

_____, and now it must be respected.
        4. (be)

Art lovers and critics of the museum's administration say that it

_____ come to this. They claim that the administration
        5. (not / have to)

_____ all it could to keep the museum profitable.
        6. (may / not / do)

"Art museums _____ make money,
                      7. (suppose)

_____ they?" asked Cheryl Rand, a city council board
        8. (be)

member. "There are many things Hall _____ over the years to
                                            9. (could / do)

keep the number of visitors up, but he _____. He
                                               10. (not / do)

_____ try something different if he wants to stay open."
        11. (got to)

Hall said the museum _____ its gift shop, which is usually
                              12. (may / expand)

more profitable than ticket sales. He also said that advertising

_____ a good way to bring more people to the museum.
        13. (could / be)

4 | EDITING: THE NEWLY RENOVATED MUSEUM

*Read this phone conversation about visiting the City Art Museum. There are ten mistakes in the use of modals, modal-like expressions, and **be** verbs and auxiliaries. The first mistake is already corrected. Find and correct nine more. (Note: There is often more than one way to correct a mistake.)*

ABBY: Hi, Liza. I'm calling to let you know when I'm coming. I ~~may~~ *should/ought to* be arriving on Friday morning.

LIZA: That's great, Abby! While you're here, you go with me to the City Art Museum. It's fantastic!

ABBY: I must appreciate art more, but I'm not really a big art fan.

LIZA: Neither I, but this museum really amazing. You like chocolate, do you?

ABBY: Of course I am.

LIZA: So am I. Well, this museum has chocolate in every room. You have seen it on the news.

ABBY: Oh, I think I hear about that. Well, OK, it sounds like it ought to be fun. See you soon!

Unit 4 Achievement Test

31 Items
Score: _____

1 | LISTENING: PACKING

🎧 **A.** *Mr. and Mrs. Park are talking about packing and moving. Listen to their conversation. Complete the conversation by writing the word(s) that you hear. You'll hear the recording two times.*

MRS. PARK: I just love packing. _____ *Don't* _____ you?
0.

MR. PARK: Are you joking? Not at all!

MRS. PARK: Well, I really do. I've always enjoyed packing. Oh, I know it's a lot of work, but I

do enjoy going through all my things and putting them in boxes. By the way,

_____ you seen the tape? I want to tape this box.
1.

MR. PARK: No, I haven't. I hope you realize that you have about three times as many clothes as

I do. _____ you think you should give away whatever you
2.

don't wear?

MRS. PARK: You're right. Maybe I should get rid of one of these jackets. Let's see, the red one is

new, but _____ is the blue one. The red one is nice to wear
3.

to work, but the blue one is too. I like that the red one doesn't have any buttons on

the sleeves, but _____ does the blue one. I just don't know.
4.

I wear them both.

MR. PARK: What about these dresses? Let's see, you do wear this flowery one, but I've never

seen you wear this brown one.

MRS. PARK: It _____ ugly, _____ it? I guess I
5. **6.**

_____ get rid of it. Let's start a box of things to give away.
7.

MR. PARK: I think I've changed my mind. I do like packing!

B. *Reread the conversation again. Then read each statement and circle* **T** *(true) or* **F** *(false).*

T **(F)** 0. Mrs. Park asks Mr. Park "Don't you?" because she wants to know if he is joking.

T **F** 1. Mr. Park knows where the tape is.

T **F** 2. The blue jacket that Mrs. Park has is not new.

T **F** 3. Mrs. Park thinks that the blue jacket is nice to wear to work.

T **F** 4. Mrs. Park likes the blue jacket because it doesn't have any buttons on the sleeves.

T **F** 5. Mrs. Park decided to give away the brown dress because it is ugly.

2 | LIVING SIMPLY

A. *The Park children are talking about packing. Complete their conversation by writing the letter of the correct form in the blanks.*

JUN: Hey Charlotte, ____*a*____ (a. did b. do c. have d. are) you see that Mom and Dad have a box
      0.

of things to give away?

SOOK: Yes, I did, but it's more like five boxes now! They are getting rid of everything! Mom's

giving all her clothes away, and Dad's getting rid of his books. I just _____ (a. didn't
      1.

b. did c. don't d. do) understand them!

JUN: They're not getting rid of *everything*, _____ (a. but they are b. so they are c. but they aren't
      2.

d. so they aren't) getting rid of a lot of stuff, _____ (a. are b. aren't c. do d. don't) they? I
      3.

think it's a great idea. They say they want to live more simply, and _____
      4.

(a. so have b. neither do c. so do d. neither have) I.

SOOK: So, what _____ (a. are b. do c. have d. did) you getting rid of?
      5.

JUN: Oh, just some stuff I don't use anymore. However, I _____ (a. doesn't b. don't c. didn't
      6.

d. do) want to take some of Dad's books!

B. *Look at the dialogue again. Then read each statement and circle the correct word.*

0. Sook (saw / didn't see) that Mom and Dad had a box of things to give away.

1. Jun (thinks / doesn't think) that Mom and Dad are getting rid of everything.

2. Jun (wants / doesn't want) to live more simply.

3. Jun (wants / doesn't want) to take some of Dad's books.

3 | MOVING TIPS

Read this advice about moving that the moving company sent the Parks. Complete the advice by writing the correct forms of **be** *verbs and auxiliaries in the blanks.*

If you _____*are*_____ getting ready to move, it may be quite stressful. Change often
0.

_____. However, if you follow these simple tips, moving can be quite easy.
1.

Tip #1: Keep plenty of supplies on hand. You're in the middle of packing, and you run out of

boxes or tape. Frustrating, _____ it? You don't want this to happen to you. Plus,
2.

keeping enough supplies on hand will save you time.

Tip #2: Label your boxes. This may seem obvious, and it _____, but it's
3.

surprising how many people don't do it when they're in a hurry. Sure, it takes a little time, but so

_____ looking for the toilet paper when you need it in your new home.
4.

Tip #3: Unload big furniture first. When you put the dressers and bookshelves in your house

first, you have a place to put your boxes. Many of our customers have thanked us for giving

them this tip, and believe me, you _____ too.
5.

Moving certainly is a stressful time, but remembering these tips _____ make it
6.

easier for you. Good luck!

4 | EDITING: UNPACKING

The Parks have moved into their new house. Read their conversation. There are five mistakes in the use of **be** *and auxiliaries. The first mistake is already corrected. Find and correct four more.*

        do
Sook: Mom, ~~did~~ you know where the box is with all my clothes?

Mrs. Park: It's in your bedroom, is it?

Sook: I just looked a minute ago, but I don't see it.

Mrs. Park: Check again. I think it does.

Sook: Oh, I found it. Hey, Mom, remember how you were going to give away your

    brown dress because you thought it was ugly? Well, it is. I love it!

Mrs. Park: So you did take it out of the box! I was wondering where it went!

Unit 5 Achievement Test

1 | LISTENING: FRIENDLY ADVICE

🎧 **A.** *Sandy is giving Dale advice on opening a seafood restaurant. Listen and complete the conversation by writing the word(s) that you hear. You'll hear the recording two times.*

DALE: So that's the restaurant. Do you like it?

SANDY: I love it! But _____ *shouldn't you have* _____ put in some smoke detectors?
   0.

DALE: They should have installed them yesterday, but they never showed up. They're supposed to come tomorrow. I ought to call and remind them about it. I

_____ forget.
   1.

SANDY: Also, I was thinking you could have different lighting. For instance, you

_____ consider using some nice lamps instead of these
   2.

fluorescent lights.

DALE: I agree, but I'm renting the building, and I _____ make changes
   3.

to the lighting. We _____, according to the contract.
   4.

SANDY: You don't have to take out the lights. You could just keep them off and use the lamps

instead.

DALE: That's a good idea. I _____ talked to you earlier!
   5.

B. *Reread the conversation. Then read each statement and circle* **T** *(true) or* **F** *(false).*

Ⓣ **F**   0. Sandy thinks that it is a good idea for Dale to install some smoke detectors in the restaurant.

T **F**   1. The people responsible for the smoke detectors came and installed them yesterday.

T **F**   2. Dale doesn't expect the people to come and install fire detectors tomorrow.

T **F**   3. It doesn't matter if Dale forgets about the smoke detector installation.

T **F**   4. Sandy suggests that Dale change the restaurant lighting.

T **F**   5. It's OK to change the lighting, according to the contract.

2 | OPEN FOR BUSINESS

A. *Complete this conversation about Dale's newly opened restaurant. Use modals from the box.*

'd better	couldn't have	~~should have~~	could have
were to	didn't have to	might	shouldn't
don't have to	had better not	was supposed to	
had to	shouldn't have		

SANDY: Hi! How's business?

DALE: Great, but I _____ *should have* _____ done so many things differently! For
　　　　　　　　　　　　　0.

　　　instance, I shouldn't have bought glass plates. They keep breaking! Now I have to buy

　　　plastic ones. Also, I _____ have air-conditioning in the kitchen,
　　　　　　　　　　　　　　　　1.

　　　but we were so busy with other things that I forgot. I just assumed that there was air-

　　　conditioning, but I could have made sure. I _____ run out
　　　　　　　　　　　　　　　　　　　　　　　　2.

　　　earlier this afternoon and buy a big fan because my cooks were almost ready to quit.

SANDY: Oh, my! You _____ take care of that first thing tomorrow.
　　　　　　　　　　　3.

DALE: I will. Also, I _____ asked for advice from more people. I
　　　　　　　　　　4.

　　　thought I didn't have to because I had my own ideas, but things

　　　_____ have gone much more smoothly if I had only asked for
　　　　　　　5.

　　　other people's opinions.

SANDY: Well, you're probably right about that. It always helps to get other people's advice when

　　　you're making big decisions like this. Hey, can I pay for lunch?

DALE: No, I already paid for you.

SANDY: Oh, thank you! You _____ do that!
　　　　　　　　　　　　　　6.

B. *Reread the conversation. Then read each statement and circle the correct word.*

0. Dale told Sandy that it (would have been)/ wouldn't have been) better if he had done many

things differently.

1. Dale (thinks / doesn't think) that buying glass plates was the right decision.

2. It (was / was not) necessary for Dale to buy a fan.

3. Dale (should / should not) have asked for advice from more people.

3	LETTER FROM THE LANDLORD

Read this letter from Ray Webb, the owner of Dale's building. Complete the letter. Use the correct forms of each modal or modal-like expression in parentheses.

Mr. Richards:

I visited your restaurant. Unfortunately, you were out buying a fan, so I could not speak with

you. However, I _____ *must bring* _____ some problems to your attention. First of all, you
          0. (must / bring)

_____ to make any changes to the structure of the building, yet I see that
        1. (not / allow)

you have taken out a wall. You _____ it back in. Second, you shouldn't
                              2. (have / put)

have added extra parking in the parking lot, but you did. There _____
                                                                3. (suppose / be)

only 20 parking spaces according to city codes. Finally, you _____ rent
                                                            4. (be / pay)

by the first of the month, but you didn't this month. You _____ by this
                                                         5. (must / pay)

Friday, or I cannot allow you to stay in the building.

Ray Webb

4 | EDITING: WHAT I'VE LEARNED

Dale wrote what he learned about running a restaurant on his personal Web page. Read his Web log. There are seven mistakes in the use of modals and modal-like expressions. The first mistake is already corrected. Find and correct six more. (Note: There is often more than one way to correct a mistake.)

My restaurant's been open for a couple of months now, and things are going much better

than they were in the beginning. I really ~~have done~~ *could/should have done* my homework better before opening my

restaurant, I admitted! Here are two things that I have learned . . .

First, I have saved enough to buy my own building for the restaurant instead of renting. My

contract said I wasn't supposed to make many of the changes that I thought were necessary, so I

have saved myself a lot of trouble if I had bought a building instead. I don't know if this could

have been possible, but I have tried.

Second, the law says I am not pay my employees without taking out city taxes. A friend of

mine told me I didn't have because the restaurant is outside the city limits, but he was wrong. So,

I've had to change the way I pay my workers.

That's all I will write for now. I'm sure I'll add more as my restaurant experience increases!

Unit 6 Achievement Test

1 | LISTENING: WORRIED MOM

🎧 **A.** *Mr. and Mrs. Jensen are wondering why their daughter, Nora, isn't home from work yet. Complete their conversation by writing the word(s) that you hear. For some items, there may be more than one blank. You'll hear the recording two times.*

MRS. JENSEN: I'm worried. Where _____*could*_____ Nora be? She couldn't still be
0.
at work. Something must be wrong!

MR. JENSEN: You're right. She can't be at work now. It's almost seven o'clock. But she
_____ just gone somewhere after work. She should be
1.
home soon.

MRS. JENSEN: She _____ tried to call us. She always calls us if she's late!
2.
Her cell phone may not be working, so she _____ able to
3.
call, but where might she be, and why _____ she
4.
_____ called from another phone? She may be hurt!

MR. JENSEN: I don't know, but it's no use worrying. She _____ be in
5.
any danger at all. She could have run into an old friend and started talking. She
_____ call or be home any minute now.
6.

B. *Reread the conversation. Then read each statement and circle the correct word.*

0. Mrs. Jensen is (almost / not) certain that something went wrong with Nora.

1. Mr. and Mrs. Jensen are certain that Nora (is / isn't) at work.

2. Mr. Jensen is (sure / not sure) that Nora is fine.

3. Mr. Jensen is (almost / not) certain that Nora will call or come home very soon.

2 | LOST CELL PHONE

A. *Read this conversation between Nora and her friend Pilar about Nora's lost cell phone. Complete the conversation. Use modals from the box.*

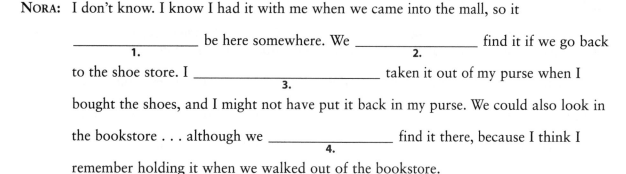

may not	should not	might not have
might	ought not to	~~could have~~
may have	may	's got to

PILAR: Where do you think you ___*could have*___ left your cell phone?
    0.

NORA: I don't know. I know I had it with me when we came into the mall, so it

   _____ be here somewhere. We _____ find it if we go back
          1.   **2.**

   to the shoe store. I _____ taken it out of my purse when I
                                  3.

   bought the shoes, and I might not have put it back in my purse. We could also look in

   the bookstore . . . although we _____ find it there, because I think I
                                            4.

   remember holding it when we walked out of the bookstore.

PILAR: I think we ought to check the bathroom.

NORA: I can't have left it in the bathroom because that was before we went to the bookstore,

   and I had it then, remember?

PILAR: Oh, yeah . . . hey, why don't you call yourself?

NORA: I could do that, but I _____ left my phone on.
                                       5.

PILAR: Oh. Well, we _____ have some luck if we just walk back the way we came
                            6.

   and look for it.

NORA: On the other hand, someone might have taken it, and we might not find it at all! Oh,

   what's the point of even looking?

PILAR: Come on, Nora. We shouldn't give up so soon. We might still find it.

B. *Reread the conversation. Then read each statement and circle* **T** *(true) or* **F** *(false).*

Ⓣ **F**   0. Pilar is not certain that Nora knew where she left her cell phone.

T **F**   1. Nora is not certain that she left her cell phone in the mall.

T **F**   2. Nora strongly doubts she put her cell back in her purse when buying the shoes.

T **F**   3. Nora is almost certain that she didn't leave her cell phone in the bathroom.

T **F**   4. It is possible that Nora will never find her cell phone.

T **F**   5. Nora had the chance to leave her phone on, but she didn't do it.

---

3 | MISSING WOMAN FOUND

The Jensens are watching the news about a missing woman. Complete the newscaster's sentences. Use the correct forms of the modals or modal-like expressions in parentheses.

Earlier today police reported that two witnesses saw a man push a woman into a car earlier

this evening. The woman was screaming. Although the witnesses couldn't see the man clearly,

they reported that the man _____*must have been*_____ tall because he had to bend down a lot
                                         0. (must / be)

to enter the car. They also reported that he _____ a dark backpack
                                                      1. (might / wear)

because he took a large object off his back before entering the car. He then drove away very fast,

and the witness thought that the man _____ because of the way he was
                                              2. (might / upset)

driving. Witnesses said they don't remember much about the car because it was snowing quite

heavily. Also, it was getting dark, and it was difficult to see. The car that was involved

_____ any dark color, and it _____ a compact
          3. (could / be)   **4. (may / be)**

size. One thing witnesses were sure about, however, was that it _____ a
                                                                       5. (could / not / be)

truck.

This just in—the police have just caught up with the "screaming woman" and her

"kidnapper" at a nearby hospital! It turns out that the woman has just delivered a baby boy, and

without her husband's race-car driving skills, they _____ in time!
                                                          6. (might / not / arrive)

4 | EDITING: JOURNAL ENTRY

Nora is upset about her mother's worrying. Read her journal entry. There are five mistakes in the use of modals and modal-like expressions. The first mistake is already corrected. Find and correct four more. (Note: There can be more than one way to correct a mistake.)

Dad yelled at me for upsetting Mom tonight. He said she was about to call the police

                                                          might have been
because I was late. At first, I thought that she ~~is~~ overreacting because I was only a couple of

hours late. But Dad told me that they had just seen a news report about a missing woman.

Then I understood how she felt—she could have been worried sick! I would have called, but I

might not have imagined that she would get so worried. I talk to her tomorrow and tell her

how it bothers me that she worries so much about me. She mustn't understand, though. She's

my Mom, so she may never stop worrying about me.

Part II Achievement Test

60 Items
Score: _____

🎧 **A.** *Eric and Kelly are shopping in the mall. Listen and complete their conversation by writing the word(s) that you hear. You'll hear the recording two times.*

ERIC: This mall has gotten old, _____*hasn't it*_____?
0.

KELLY: It has gotten old! It _____ been one of the first malls ever built.
1.

They really must improve it if they want more business.

ERIC: You're right. _____ buy a gift for your dad's birthday?
2.

KELLY: Yeah. The department store could have the tool set he's been looking for. We

_____ go take a look. They may not have exactly what he
3.

wants, but I saw an advertisement for something like what he was looking for. At least I

think I _____.
4.

ERIC: Watch that hole in the floor! You _____ fallen in it! That other
5.

lady almost fell in it too. It was pure luck that she _____. I think
6.

we should tell an employee that they need to cover the hole, don't you?

KELLY: Yes, I _____! The mall staff _____ be
7.   8.

aware of it. I'm just amazed no one has fallen in it yet.

ERIC: So am I. You know, the other day I read an article about all the problems with public

safety in places like this. Most people don't seem to worry much about how dangerous

these places _____ be, but I do.
9.

KELLY: So _____ I! I'm afraid the staff here in the mall might not do
10.

anything about the hole. No one seems to care about this place, and someone

_____ get hurt. We _____ tolerate it. I
11.   12.

might e-mail someone on the city council about this when I get home.

ERIC: Good idea. I will too. They _____ allowed to stay open like this.
13.

B. *Reread the conversation. Then read each statement and circle* **T** *(true) or* **F** *(false).*

Ⓣ **F**   **0.** Eric thinks that the mall has gotten old.

T **F**   **1.** Kelly is absolutely certain that the mall is one of the first malls ever built.

T **F**   **2.** Eric needs to buy a gift for his dad's birthday.

T **F**   **3.** It is a good idea for Kelly to look for the tool set at the department store.

T **F**   **4.** It is OK for the mall to remain in this condition.

T **F**   **5.** Kelly is not certain that she can find the tool set her father's been looking for in the department store.

T **F**   **6.** Both Eric and Kelly agree that they should tell an employee about the hole.

T **F**   **7.** Kelly is absolutely certain that employees do not know about the hole.

T **F**   **8.** Kelly was amazed no one had fallen in the hole yet, but Eric wasn't.

T **F**   **9.** Neither Eric nor Kelly cares much about the safety in the mall.

T **F** **10.** It is possible for people to get hurt in the mall.

---

2 | E-MAIL TO CITY COUNCIL

A. *Eric has written an e-mail to the city council about his visit to the mall. Complete the e-mail. Use the appropriate modals or phrases from the box.*

haven't	should not	so can	might
are to	couldn't have been	neither can	shouldn't have
had better not	~~are you~~	don't have to	
might not	should	can't have been	

Dear City Council:

    I went to Central Mall today. A lot of people don't seem to be aware of the situation there.

_____ *Are you* _____? Maybe not. You _____ be mall
        0.   **1.**

shoppers. Or, maybe you are mall shoppers, but you _____ been to the
                                                       2.

mall recently. That's true for many of us. In any case, I wanted to let you know that I found some

major problems. They were so bad that I thought they _____ real and
                                                            3.

that maybe I dreamed the whole thing!

The mall probably _____ even be open because it is old and

dangerous. You could go there yourself and see what I mean. It _____

renovated since it opened, and people _____ get hurt. Why haven't the

city safety inspectors done anything about this? They must not have visited this mall in years! I

think you _____ talk with someone in management at the mall. Maybe

they _____ close for good, but they _____ be

allowed to stay open the way they are.

I can visit with you in your office if you have any questions for me. _____

my wife. We will be happy to answer any questions you might have.

Sincerely yours,

Eric Banghart

B. *Reread the e-mail. Then read each statement and circle the correct word(s).*

0. Eric (is / (is not)) certain if the city council members are mall shoppers.

1. Eric (found / didn't find) some real problems with the mall.

2. It (is / is not) OK for the mall to be open because it has safety problems.

3. It (would / would not) be a good idea if the city council could talk with someone in

   management to solve the problem.

4. Eric is fairly certain that the city safety inspector (has / has not) been there lately.

5. Eric and his wife (can / cannot) visit the city council office.

3 | MALL SUFFERS FINANCIAL CRISIS

*Read this newspaper article about the future of Central Mall. Complete the article. Use the correct forms of the modals, modal-like expressions, **be** verbs, or auxiliaries in parentheses.*

Central Mall _____*could be closing*_____ its doors by the end of the year,
0. (could / close)

according to mall administrator, Tom Henderson, if the staff is not able to improve safety.

City Council has voted that the mall _____ stay open if
1. (must / not)

people are getting hurt, which they _____. Many people have
2. (be)

said that the mall _____ open this long.
3. (should / not / remain)

Shoppers and critics of the mall administration say that the mall _____
4. (not / have to)

become as unsafe as it has. They say that the administration _____ all it
5. (might / not / do)

could to keep the mall safe.

"All public places _____ be as safe as possible,
6. (suppose)

_____ they?" asked Howard Grand, a City Council board member.
7. (be)

"There are many things Henderson _____ over the years to keep the
8. (could / do)

mall safe, but he _____. He _____ action if he
9. (do)   **10. (must / take)**

wants to stay open."

Henderson said the mall will address the big problems. First, they _____
11. (have to / repair)

the holes. Then they _____ the floors. Finally, they _____
12. (may / retile)   **13. (might / ask)**

the city for financial support to remodel the mall.

4 | EDITING: MALL REOPENS

Read this phone conversation about going to the mall. There are ten mistakes in the use of modals, modal-like expressions, and **be** *verbs and auxiliaries. The first mistake is already corrected. Find and correct nine more. (Note: There can be more than one way to correct a mistake.)*

TINA: Hi, Kelly. I just want to let you know when I'm coming. I'm leaving my house Saturday

                              ought to/should

        morning at 9:00. I ~~might~~ arrive at your house by 11:00.

KELLY: Great! While you're here, you go with me to the mall. It's fantastic!

TINA: Well . . . I am not allowed to say no, but you know that I don't enjoy shopping much.

KELLY: Neither I, but this mall really incredible. You're not against free food, aren't you?

TINA: Of course I don't.

KELLY: Neither do I. Well, this mall has free food this Saturday to celebrate its reopening. You

        have seen it in the news.

TINA: I don't watch the news much, so I probably don't heard about it. I am interested, though.

        See you Saturday!

PART III Diagnostic Test

1 | LISTENING: ANIMAL SHELTER ADVERTISEMENT

🎧 **A.** *Listen to this radio advertisement for an animal shelter. Complete the advertisement by writing the word(s) that you hear. You will hear the recording two times.*

Have you hugged _____ *a dog* _____ today? Have you pet
          0.

_____? Central City Animal Shelter has many pets that need the love and
   1.

attention of a new owner and friend. The cats and dogs at our shelter have been displaced and

need _____. For many people, owning _____
     2.   **3.**

can be one of life's _____ experiences. By adopting a pet, you'll be giving
                4.

one of these animals a _____, and the animal you take home may truly
               5.

become your best friend. _____ animal up for adoption is healthy and
               6.

disease free. We're conveniently located just east of Central Park. Come visit us today.

B. *Reread the radio advertisement. Then read each statement and circle **T** (true) or **F** (false).*

Ⓣ **F**   0. Some animals are waiting for adoption.

T **F**   1. The Central City Animal Shelter needs new owners.

T **F**   2. The Central City Animal Shelter is for displaced animals.

T **F**   3. The Central City Animal Shelter wants to find new homes for their cats or
             dogs.

T **F**   4. A lot of people find having an animal at home to be a nice experience.

T **F**   5. You can give the animals a new life if you adopt them.

T **F**   6. An animal you adopt might become your best friend.

T **F**   7. A few of the animals up for adoption are sick.

T **F**   8. Central Park is close to the Central City Animal Shelter.

2 | PET THERAPY

Complete this magazine article about pet therapy. Use the words and phrases from the box.

life	~~most enjoyable ways~~	animal friends	more
pet	a healthy choice	a great deal of	the music
stress	highly positive influence	stress-related	music
the	conversation	chance of survival	some
any	heart-warming		

One of the easiest and _____ *most enjoyable ways* _____ to improve your quality of

0.

life may be to own a _____. In fact, there is

1.

_____ evidence from numerous studies that show why

2.

owning a pet may be _____ for many

3.

_____ problems.

4.

For instance, petting a dog or cat can lower your heart rate and actually reduce

_____. One study showed that watching a tank full of tropical

5.

fish can be as calming as listening to _____. In addition, heart

6.

attack victims with _____ at home have a 21 percent greater

7.

_____ the year after a heart attack than those who do not own

8.

pets. Periodically, you'll even hear a _____ story in the news

9.

about how a pet has saved its owner's life.

Better physical health is not the only benefit of pets. Pets can have a

_____ on people's emotional health as well. Some people think

10.

that pets can really act like therapists even though they cannot have a

_____. Pets have also been found to bring

11.

_____ laughter and pleasure to the elderly in nursing homes

12.

than any other therapy.

Given _____ many benefits that pets can have, is there

13.

_____ reason not to own a pet?

14.

_____ people may be allergic to animals. Others may live in
                                15.

places that do not allow pets. However, if you are able to have a pet, getting one could change

your life for the better.

---

3 | THE GREATEST GIFT

Read this article from the Internet about Roman Jaworski and his dog, Coco. Complete the
article with the correct answers. Write the letter of the best answer on each line.

When Roman Jaworski, ____*a*____ (**a. a Polish immigrant b. the Polish immigrant c. Polish immigrant**
                        0.

d. Polish immigrants) to the United States, was diagnosed with a rare _____ (**a. form of the cancer**
                                                                      1.

b. form of cancer c. cancers d. form of cancers) at the age of 37, he gave up hope. He quit his job and

began to sleep _____ (**a. most b. most of the c. much d. many of the**) day. Some days, he never even
              2.

got out of bed. Then one day, _____ (**a. the second chance b. second chance c. some second chance**
                              3.

d. a second chance) at life put her paws on Roman's front porch. Roman immediately fell in love

with the _____ (**a. long hair b. long hairs c. long-haired d. long-hair**) dog that showed up at his
         4.

door. Coco, who is the color of _____ (**a. milk chocolate b. milked chocolate c. milk-chocolated**
                                5.

d. milked-chocolated), helped Roman to come out of his deep depression. Today, Roman takes Coco

for a walk twice a day along the beaches of Santa Cruz, California, his hometown on _____
                                                                                   6.

(**a. Pacific Ocean b. Pacific Oceans c. the Pacific Ocean d. the Pacific Oceans**). Roman is working again

_____ (**a. a great deal of b. a little c. less d. a few**) hours a week, and he spends a lot of his free time
7.

at home with Coco and playing _____ (**a. the guitar b. guitar c. a guitar d. guitars**). Roman says
                               8.

that Coco changed his life because she has given him the _____ (**a. great very gift b. very greatest**
                                                         9.

gift c. gift very great d. gift very greatest), the gift of love. As _____ (**a. Poles b. a Pole c. the Poles**
                                                                      10.

d. any Poles) say, "Only a mother's love is greater than a dog's."

4 | LITTLE HERO

Read this newspaper article about a heroic dog. Complete the article. Use the correct form of each word or phrase. Some items may have more than one possible answer. (Note: Put the words in parentheses in the correct order and add articles [a/an, the] if necessary.)

Laurens Vanderhoff of Amsterdam would not be alive today if it weren't for his

_____*six-pound terrier, Albert*_____. The _____ is
 0. (six pounds / Albert / terrier)   1. (white / small / dog)

credited with saving the life of his _____ owner,
                                                        2. (42 years old)

_____, who suffers from the disease characterized by increased
 3. (diabetic)

levels of sugar in the blood. Last Tuesday, Mr. Vanderhoff's blood sugar got too high, and he fell

unconscious in his _____. The tiny dog barked until a
                                4. (house)

neighbor came to see what was the matter. _____, Pieter
                                                                  5. (neighbor)

Keese, called the paramedics, who revived the man. Keese called Albert

"_____." He said, "Albert doesn't usually bark, so when he
 6. (incredible / wonderful / dog)

made so much noise, I knew something was wrong. There's no question Albert saved Mr.

Vanderhoff's life."

   Sofie Oudekirk, a veterinary doctor in _____, says this is
                                                              7. (Netherlands)

not the first time a dog has saved the life of its diabetic owner. She said that some dogs use their

_____ of smell to detect the level of
 8. (sense / keen)

_____ in their owner's blood. They can alert the person or
 9. (sugar)

others by barking if _____ is too high. "Thanks to their dogs,"
                                  10. (sugar / level)

she says, "some diabetics get _____ at life."
                                              11. (second / chance)

5 | EDITING: THE OPERA-SINGING PARROT

Read this paragraph about an opera-singing parrot. There are 11 mistakes in the use of nouns, articles, quantifiers, and modification of nouns. The first mistake is already corrected. Find and correct 10 more. (Note: There can be more than one way to correct a mistake.)

          talented
Polly Chord is a remarkably ~~talent~~ musician. But so are many people, so why is Polly interesting? Because Polly isn't a person—she is a 37 years old parrot, and she sings an opera. Among her favorites are "Quand je vous aimerai" from Bizet's *Carmen* and "O Mio Babbino Caro" from Puccini's *Gianni Schicchi*. It is not unusual for parrot to sing opera if they hear it enough, but what is unusual is pure joy Polly seems to get from singing it. As she sings, her pupils dilate, she fluffs her green yellow and red feathers, and she stretches her wings and spins around as though she were dancing. She displays same enthusiasm over cup of apple sauce, her favorite food. Polly has not had some formal musical training, but she has developed a love of singing opera on her own. Few of Polly's other vocal talents, though less noteworthy, include imitating a rooster and the sound of the doorbell.

Unit 7 Achievement Test

1 | LISTENING: FIRST DAY OF CLASS

🎧 **A.** *Listen to an introduction to a chemistry course. Complete the introduction by writing the word(s) that you hear. You will hear the recording two times.*

Welcome to _____<u>Chemistry</u>_____ 101. My name is Dr. Smith. This semester you will
                  0.

experiment with oxygen, hydrogen, air, _____, sugar, and energy, as well as other
                                                  1.

natural phenomena. You will also learn Mendeleev's periodic table of elements. A course project

is required, but you will have some _____ to choose your own topics. Students are
                                           2.

expected to be in their _____ when the bell rings and to hand in homework
                           3.

_____ on time. I hope we'll have some _____ this semester.
       4.   **5.**

B. *Reread the introduction to the course. Write each noun from the box below in the correct category. One category may not have any nouns.*

bell	hydrogen	semester
Dr. Smith	~~name~~	sugar
energy	phenomena	topics

CATEGORIES	NOUNS
1. Count nouns	name,
2. Proper nouns	
3. Count nouns with irregular plurals	
4. Non-count nouns in countable form	
5. Non-count nouns	

2 | COUNT AND NON-COUNT NOUNS

Read each sentence. Write **C** *if the underlined word is a count noun and* **N** *if it is a non-count noun.*

___N___ **0.** Many families play <u>cards</u> together.

_____ **1.** It is often difficult to explain human <u>behavior</u>.

_____ **2.** We had a good <u>conversation</u>.

_____ **3.** Many people die of <u>cancer</u> every year.

_____ **4.** We have a <u>responsibility</u> to care for the elderly.

_____ **5.** The professor has given several <u>talks</u> about his study.

_____ **6.** A major contributor to the greenhouse effect is <u>carbon dioxide</u>.

_____ **7.** The risk of <u>heart disease</u> can be lowered by diet and exercise.

_____ **8.** <u>Soccer</u> is one of the most popular sports in the world.

3 | NON-COUNT NOUNS IN COUNTABLE FORM

Complete each sentence with one word to make the non-count noun countable. The first letter of each word is provided.

0. Sometimes an old p*iece* _____ of furniture can be worth a lot of money.

1. It was dark and stormy, and suddenly there was a f_____ of lightening.

2. She cut off a p_____ of meat and began to chew it slowly.

3. Several g_____ of rice fell to the floor while she was cooking.

4. Let's play a g_____ of tennis.

4 | EDITING: COLLEGE TALK

Read this conversation between two college students. There are six mistakes in the use of nouns. The first mistake is already corrected. Find and correct five more. (Note: There can be more than one way to correct a mistake.)

                    economics/an economics class

ED: Are you taking ~~an economics~~ this semester?

JULIE: No, I'm taking a history with Mr. anderson instead.

ED: Oh, I took his class. I really like him, but some peoples don't.

JULIE: I like him. Right now we're reading about the native people of Australia, like the Djiki Manunu and the Djikirritipi. The class is really interesting, but it takes times to do all the readings.

Unit 8 Achievement Test

30 Items
Score: _____

1 | LISTENING: THE FUTURE OF TECHNOLOGY

🎧 **A.** *Listen to the introduction to a TV program about the future of technology. Complete the introduction by writing the word(s) that you hear. You will hear the recording two times.*

Welcome to *Science and Society.* _____*The development*_____ of
0.

_____ relies on previous knowledge, discoveries, and inventions. For
1.

example, one of _____ in the world is the Internet. However, the Internet
2.

couldn't exist without knowing about _____ and the computer first.
3.

Another example is the cell phone, which uses previous inventions such as batteries, the

telephone, and _____. No one knows what the next big invention will
4.

be. It could be a machine that transports you across the globe within seconds, much like

_____! On today's show, we'll be looking at the future of technology.
5.

B. *Read the sentences based on the introduction to the TV program. For each sentence, classify the underlined word or phrase as indefinite (I), definite (D), or generic (G).*

__G__ **0.** Previous discoveries such as <u>electricity</u> lay the foundation for future ones.

_____ **1.** Welcome to <u>*Science and Society*</u>.

_____ **2.** I would like to buy <u>a computer</u>.

_____ **3.** <u>The Internet</u> is an important invention of the 20th century.

_____ **4.** The Internet wouldn't have been possible without <u>the computer</u>.

_____ **5.** We don't know what <u>the next big invention</u> will be.

_____ **6.** On today's show, we'll be looking at <u>the future</u> of technology.

_____ **7.** <u>The cell phone</u> is also a great invention.

_____ **8.** The next big invention could be <u>a machine</u> that transports you across the globe within

seconds.

2 | HYDROGEN CARS

Complete this conversation about hydrogen fuel cars. Use the words from the box.

the ~~future~~	an invention	Dr. Tanner	a guy
time	an energy revolution	revolution	problems
a company	hydrogen cars		

JIM: Did you see that program last night about _____ *the future* _____ of

0.

technology?

NICOLE: No, I was at the office. Was it good?

JIM: Yeah, it was one of the best shows I've seen recently. They interviewed

_____ who works for _____ called

1. **2.**

Naxpron Technologies. He was saying that hydrogen fuel cars will be commercially

available within the next few years.

NICOLE: Oh, we talked about _____ in class. Our professor,

3.

_____, thinks we're going to experience

4.

_____. She said the revolution will change the way we drive,

5.

but others in the class think there are still many _____ with the

6.

technology. I guess only _____ will tell.

7.

3 | WILDLIFE IN NATIONAL PARKS

Read this paragraph from a visitor's brochure about one kind of animal in a national park.
Complete the paragraph. Use the correct definite or indefinite article with each noun or
phrase.

Have you ever seen a _____ *a buffalo/buffaloes* _____? At one time,

0. (buffalo)

_____ was one of _____ in

1. (buffalo) **2. (most common mammals)**

_____. However, by the early 1830s, they had become extinct east of the

3. (United States)

Mississippi River. Since then many people have worked to protect these animals, and now the

population has made _____. There are an estimated 200,000 buffaloes

4. (comeback)

living in this country today, and our national park is home to many of them.

4 | EDITING: HYDROGEN POWER FOR YACHTS

Read the paragraph about another use for hydrogen power. There are seven mistakes in the use of definite and indefinite articles. The first mistake is already corrected. Find and correct six more.

You may have heard of ~~hydrogen car,~~ *hydrogen cars/a hydrogen car* but have you heard of a hydrogen boat? Yacht manufacturer has created a new hydrogen-powered yacht called *The Agua Limpia*. Yacht makes use of clean energy that converts hydrogen and oxygen into the water. This technology could make the sailing possible without polluting planet's waters. It's some of most exciting technology in recent news.

PART III

Unit 9 Achievement Test

30 Items
Score: _____

🎧 **A.** *Listen to the radio commentary about going paperless. Complete the commentary by writing the word(s) that you hear. You will hear the recording two times.*

I love paper. I probably have _____*enough*_____ paper on my desk to cover the walls of my
0.

house. So I was _____ concerned when I heard some talk about making our office
1.

paperless. _____ offices are becoming paperless, which means using and wasting
2.

_____ papers. But do _____ of these offices really work? According
3.   **4.**

to Howard Foster, an office managing consultant, a great many of these so-called paperless

offices are not really paperless at all. For example, you might think that e-mail reduces the need

for paper. But Foster claims that _____ offices actually increase their quantity of
5.

printing after getting e-mail connections. The increased amount of information that people

receive creates _____ demand for the information in its familiar black-and-white,
6.

portable form. In addition, paperless offices require _____ ongoing
7.

training to keep information from getting lost in cyberspace. Foster thinks that paperless offices

are both possible and efficient. But he points out that the system takes some getting used to,

especially for people like me.

B. *Read the sentences based on the radio commentary. Write the letter of the statement that correctly explains the meaning of each sentence.*

___*a*___ **0.** I use a lot of paper in my office.
     a. I use plenty of paper in my office.
     b. I use most paper in my office.

_____ **1.** I have enough paper on my desk to cover the walls of my house.
     a. I have some paper on my desk.
     b. I have a lot of paper on my desk.

_____ **2.** I heard some talk in my office about going paperless.
     a. There was a talk about going paperless in my office.
     b. Some people in my office talked about going paperless.

_____ **3.** A great many of these so-called paperless offices are not really paperless at all.
     a. Very few of these so-called paperless offices are actually paperless.
     b. A lot of these so-called paperless offices are really paperless.

_____ **4.** Some offices have little use for e-mail.

      a. Few offices prefer e-mail communication to paper.

      b. Some offices don't use e-mail communication a lot.

_____ **5.** Offices that use e-mail increase their quantity of printing a great deal.

      a. Offices use their printers a lot more after they get e-mail.

      b. Offices with e-mail use less paper than traditional offices.

---

2 | PAPERLESS TAX RETURNS

*Read one listener's response to the radio commentary and look at the following sentences based on the response. Could they be rewritten using the words in parentheses without changing the basic meaning of the sentence? Write **Y** for Yes and **N** for No.*

    Some companies have been able to make money by helping people go paperless. For example, in the late 1990s, a few companies in the United States developed software that helped people to file their taxes electronically. Unfortunately, some of the software programs had problems, and some people's tax files were lost. Once companies were able to work out most of the problems, however, many consumers were interested in paperless tax filing again. If these software programs make filing taxes easier, then I'm all for them.

  _N_ **0.** *Most* people like to file their taxes electronically. (Some)

_____ **1.** *A few* businesses have been able to incorporate some paperless elements into their

      business. (A great many)

_____ **2.** Sometimes incorporating paperless elements into business can generate *more* revenue in

      the process. (fewer)

_____ **3.** The software companies fixed *most of* the problems with the tax filing programs.

      (plenty of)

_____ **4.** *A great many* people wanted to try paperless tax filing a second time. (A lot of)

_____ **5.** *Many* consumers are interested in filing their taxes electronically. (A great deal of)

_____ **6.** If paperless tax filing is easier than the traditional way, I *don't* have *any* complaints. (no)

PART III

3 | PAPERLESS CLASSROOM

Read this news report about a paperless classroom. Complete the report with the correct quantifiers. Write the letter of the best answer on each line.

Students in one middle school classroom haven't picked up ___*a*___ (a. any b. some c. much)
                                                              0.

books all year. Instead, _____ (a. every b. each c. most) of Kate Peterson's sixth-grade students
                          1.

carries a pocket computer. There is _____ (a. little b. few c. a little) need for backpacks and
                                    2.

lockers here. Sound expensive? It's not. Peterson saves the school money by not having to buy

textbooks or make photocopies. She also says she has _____ (a. fewer b. any c. less) homework
                                                     3.

to take home at the end of the day, and she spends less time grading it.

According to Peterson, the students took _____ (a. some b. any c. no) time to get used to the
                                         4.

computers, but now they have few problems. It goes without saying that these students are

getting lots of exposure to computer technology. Indeed, _____ (a. enough of b. a great deal of
                                                         5.

c. many of) them say they want to work with computers when they grow up.

But going paperless may not work in _____ (a. every b. all c. most) classroom. Few other
                                    6.

schools have made textbooks available online, and even fewer would be able to acquire pocket

computers for each student. Nevertheless, there is _____ (a. a great many b. a great deal of
                                                   7.

c. many a) potential for integrating computers into classrooms in other ways.

4 | EDITING: SURVEY

Read this magazine article that reports the results of a survey. There are six mistakes in the use of quantifiers. The first mistake is already corrected. Find and correct five more. (Note: There can be more than one way to correct a mistake.)

Business Weekly conducted a survey of nearly 1,000 employees working at 200 self-described "paperless offices" worldwide. ~~Few~~ *Little* research has been done in this area, and much of us here at the magazine were surprised at the results. We found that a great deal of these offices still use some paper. Only 12 percent of the employees we talked to said that they use less than one sheet of paper at work per day. Even less of the people told us that they use no paper at all. A little of them work for companies where paper is prohibited. Among the employees who work in truly paperless offices, 70 percent reported missing paper a lot, 20 percent miss paper little, and only 10 percent do not miss paper at all. These results indicate that paperless offices may not be for everyone.

Unit 10 Achievement Test

30 Items
Score: _____

1 | LISTENING: ACKERLY MANSION

🎧 ***A.*** *Listen to a radio advertisement for Ackerly Mansion. Complete the advertisement by writing the word(s) that you hear. You will hear the recording two times.*

Come visit the _____*historic*_____ Ackerly Mansion. Located in the heart of charming
                              0.

downtown Minneapolis, the newly reopened Ackerly Mansion is an _____ jewel of
                                                                        1.

the Midwest. Guided tours are offered daily from 10 A.M. to 4 P.M., Monday through Saturday.

As a special event, Edward Ackerly's granddaughter, Susan Mann, will share personal family

stories and photographs this Saturday from 12 to 2. You'll learn more about the exciting,

_____ past of the Ackerly family and about their _____ influence on
        2.   **3.**

the early pioneer history of Minneapolis. Following the storytelling, fresh muffins and

_____ ice cream will be served in the mansion's spacious _____
        4.   **5.**

parlor, and there will be a band and dancing in the _____ hall. For more
                                                              6.

information, call 555-2672.

B. *Read the sentences based on the advertisement. Write the letter of the statement that correctly explains the meaning of each underlined word or phrase.*

__*a*__ **0.** Come visit the <u>historic</u> Ackerly Mansion.
       a. Ackerly Mansion has a long history.
       b. Ackerly Mansion is a historical site where important things happened.

_____ **1.** Ackerly Mansion is located in the heart of <u>charming downtown</u> Minneapolis.
       a. Downtown Minneapolis is a pleasant place.
       b. Downtown Minneapolis is very attractive because Ackerly Mansion is there.

_____ **2.** The <u>newly reopened</u> Ackerly Mansion is a jewel of the Midwest.
       a. The Ackerly Mansion was new when it first opened to the public.
       b. Ackerly Mansion had been opened to the public before.

_____ **3.** <u>Guided</u> tours are offered daily from 10 A.M. to 4 P.M., Monday through Saturday.
       a. Tour guides can show you around the mansion.
       b. Guides can answer your questions about tours.

_____ **4.** You'll learn about the Ackerly family's important influence on the <u>early pioneer</u> history
       of Minneapolis.
       a. The Ackerly family influenced important pioneers in Minneapolis.
       b. The Ackerly family was one of the pioneer families in the early history of
          Minneapolis.

2 | WASSER CASTLE

Read this Internet description of Wasser Castle. Complete the sentences with the correct phrases. Write the best answer on each line.

The _____ *elegant Wasser Castle* _____ is situated in the
    0. (Castle Wasser elegant / elegant Wasser Castle)

_____ along the Rhine River. One of the most
  1. (German heartland / heartland German)

_____ in the world, the structure is a rare example of
  2. (castles beautiful / beautiful castles)

_____. It has remained virtually unchanged since it was
3. (13th-architecture century / 13th-century architecture)

first built. Wasser Castle was an important stronghold for _____
                                          4. (rulers early / early rulers)

of the region. The _____ castle lends a
      5. (situated strategically / strategically situated)

_____ of the
  6. (view breathtaking / breathtaking view)

_____. Click here to book a tour.
7. (beautiful surroundings forested / beautiful forested surroundings)

PART III

3 | IN OTHER WORDS...

Rewrite the following phrases so that the modifier comes before the head noun. Place hyphens where they are needed.

0. an apple that is red and big

   a big red apple _____

1. a house that has two stories

   _____

2. a product that won an award

   _____

3. stones that are from Brazil and are round and purple

   _____

4. homes that are decorated beautifully

   _____

5. a dress that is blue and is made from cotton

   _____

6. a program that was approved by the government

   _____

7. a film that is old and boring and was made in France

   _____

8. a flavor that lasts a long time

   _____

4 | EDITING: POSTCARD FROM WASSER CASTLE

Read this postcard from Wasser Castle. There are six mistakes in the use of modification of nouns. The first mistake is already corrected. Find and correct five more. (Note: Mistakes may include the use of punctuation.)

Dear Doug,

                        famous Wasser Castle

    I'm writing from ~~Wasser Castle famous~~ in Germany. I was amazing to learn that the castle

is over 1,000 years old! This is just one of the many beautiful historic places I've visited so

far. It has been so excited for me to visit such wonderful interesting places. I bought a great

book that has prize winning pictures of many places I've seen. I'll show you when I get home.

Aaron

PART III

Part III Achievement Test

---

1 | LISTENING: ADVERTISEMENT FOR A HOME-BASED BUSINESS

🎧 **A.** *Listen to this radio advertisement for a nutritional supplements home business. Complete the advertisement by writing the word(s) that you hear. You will hear the recording two times.*

Did you take _____*a vitamin*_____ today? Are you one of the millions of people
0.

who take nutritional supplements? Nutritional supplements are a multi-billion dollar

_____, and now you can get your share of the sales by owning your own
1.

home-based Nutri store. For _____ people, running a business from
2.

home is an extremely _____ enterprise. We're talking about a lot of
3.

money here, so take advantage of this _____. Call now and receive a free
4.

video that describes _____ that has made thousands of people wealthy
5.

beyond their wildest _____. Every caller within the next 10 minutes will
6.

also receive a Healthy Living Pac absolutely free. Call now!

B. *Reread the radio advertisement. Then read each statement and circle* **T** *(true) or* **F** *(false).*

Ⓣ **F**   0. Millions of people take nutritional supplements.

T **F**   1. Nutritional supplements are a big business.

T **F**   2. If you own your own Nutri business, you can make a lot of money.

T **F**   3. The video explains how people make a lot of money when they own their own homes.

T **F**   4. You will receive a free video about dreams if you call now.

T **F**   5. People who call 10 minutes after the advertisement will receive a free video and a free Healthy Living Pac.

T **F**   6. Nutritional supplements are especially for wealthy people.

T **F**   7. Thousands of people have already made lots of money by participating in Nutri business.

T **F**   8. Everybody who is interested should call right now.

2 | MEAT IRRADIATION

Complete this information from the Internet about irradiating meat. Use words and phrases from the box.

few	a final criticism	~~most controversial issues~~
a process	hand-washing	possibility
the	most of	the safest way
radiation	some	food-related
no	the first result	two-time recipient
less	highly rigorous studies	criteria

One of the ___most controversial issues___ in food safety recently has been the irradiation of
                          0.

meat. Irradiation uses radiation to eliminate bacteria in raw meat. It is

_____ that can kill _____ the bacteria present.
           1.   **2.**

So what's the controversy all about? Some people argue that irradiation is

_____ to prevent many _____ illnesses, while
           3.   **4.**

others fear that the _____ may have undesirable effects.
                              5.

Professor Isaac Rosenblum, a _____ of The National Health and
                                        6.

Education Award, argues that the _____ of food poisoning does not
                                            7.

necessarily decrease with irradiation, since people who handle the meat may feel that general

sanitation and good _____ practices are no longer necessary when the
                              8.

meat is irradiated. In addition, there is _____ criticism that the high cost
                                                    9.

of irradiating meat will lead to higher meat prices and _____
                                                                    10.

consumption of meat, which could hurt the ranching industry. _____ is
                                                                          11.

that some of the nutrients found in meat are destroyed by radiation.

However, the U.S. Food and Drug Administration has conducted _____
                                                                          12.

to learn more about the effects of meat irradiation. The results look good: They have found that

there are very _____ negative results when people eat irradiated meat
                        13.

and have concluded that _____ practice is in accordance with established
                                  14.

_____ for protecting public health.
           15.

3 | GENETICALLY MODIFIED FOODS

Read this magazine article about genetically modified foods. Complete the passage with the correct answers. Write the letter of the best answer on each line.

Genetically modified foods, or GM foods, are another ___*a*___ (a. area b. result c. reason
0.

d. solution) of food safety that is lively with debate. On the one hand, genetic modification can

enhance the nutritional value and production of some kinds of food. For example, one type

of _____ (a. genetically engineer rice b. genetically engineered rice c. genetic engineered rice
1.

d. genetic engineer rice) that can help many people avoid vitamin B deficiency has received

_____ (a. few praise b. many praise c. much praise d. few praises). On the other hand, there can be
2.

problems with GM foods. For example, pollen from a _____ (a. scientific alteration
3.

b. scientifically alteration c. scientific altered d. scientifically altered) strain of corn grown in the

Midwestern United States killed many _____ (a. honey bees b. honey bee c. the honey bee
4.

d. the honey bee), a fact that outraged _____ (a. publics b. public c. the publics d. the public).
5.

Many people in the European Union are now demanding that _____ (a. food label
6.

b. food labels c. foods label d. foods labels) identify genetically modified ingredients. At the present

time, however, _____ (a. a many b. great many c. little d. few) companies have done so. This is
7.

largely because GM foods have a _____ (a. rather negative stigma b. negative rather stigma
8.

c. rather negatively stigma d. negatively rather stigma), even though every GM product in _____
9.

(a. groceries store b. grocery store c. grocery stores d. the groceries store) has undergone thorough testing

for quality and safety. Judy Arnett has studied GM foods for two decades, and she believes that

"GM foods may be the greatest advancement in food safety since the invention of _____
10.

(a. a refrigerator b. the refrigerator c. some refrigerators d. many refrigerators)."

4 | FOOD PRESERVATION

Read this Internet article about food preservation. Complete the article. Use the correct form of each word or phrase. (Note: Put the words in parentheses in the correct order and add articles [a/an, the] if necessary.)

_____Food preservation_____ is _____ with roots as ancient as
　　0. (food preservation)　　　　　　　　　　1. (art)

_____. For instance, _____ of salted meat and
　　2. (mankind)　　　　　　　　　　3. (large / barrel)

fish was found in what is now _____ near the Persian Gulf. Researchers
　　　　　　　　　　4. (United Arab Emirates)

were surprised to learn that _____ was thousands of years old. Pickling,
　　　　　　　　　5. (barrel)

which uses _____ of salt and vinegar, is another
　　　　6. (combination)

_____ of food preservation that has existed for centuries. Both of these
　　7. (method)

_____ methods kill any bacteria that may be present, preserving
　　8. (ancient / natural)

_____ for many years. In addition to these ancient methods, there are
　　9. (food)

_____ chemicals that are often found in store-bought foods, such as
　　10. (few)

sorbic acid and sodium benzoate, that help prevent _____.
　　　　　　　　　　　　　　　　　　11. (bacterial / dangerous / growth)

5 | EDITING: ANTIDEPRESSANT DRUGS

Read this paragraph in a brochure about antidepressant drugs. There are 11 mistakes in the use of nouns, articles, quantifiers, and modification of nouns. The first mistake is already corrected. Find and correct 10 more.

　　　　　　　　　　　　　　the
At any given time in ∧ United States, about 10 million people are experiencing the clinical depression. Although psychological counseling and lifestyle changes are very effective in treating depression, chemical and natural drugs may also be an important part of treatments. No one antidepressant drug is considered the most effective for everyone. Rather, the best drug for an individual is the one with the least negative side effects for him or her. Some drugs can have the side unwanted effects of sleeplessness and weight gain. There is even chance that some antidepressant drugs can make depression worse. One natural alternative remedy is St. John's Wort, which usually has a lower cost and few side effects than prescription drugs. Side effect most commonly associated with St. John's Wort is dry mouth. There is a 2,500 years old history of using this herb in Europe. It is available from Nutri without a prescription as tea, as an oil, or in capsules.

PART IV Diagnostic Test

1 | LISTENING: THE FIRST MOVIE CAMERA

🎧 *A. Listen to this radio broadcast about the first movie camera. Complete the passage by writing the word(s) that you hear. You will hear the recording two times.*

The Lumière brothers, _____*working*_____ in their father's photographic film factory,
                                    0.

invented the first working movie camera. The contributions they made to film were significant. It

was 1895 when they produced the movie camera, a nonworking prototype _____
                                                                              1.

was brought to them from New York by their father, a wealthy manufacturer. The prototype,

_____ cost nearly a million dollars in today's money, drove the brothers to develop
        2.

a more inexpensive version of the movie camera. When the camera was complete, the first movie,

directed by the Lumière brothers themselves, showed their father's workers _____
                                                                                    3.

out of the factory, the same factory that the brothers worked in, at the end of the day. Another

part of the film, starring their father's gardener being sprayed in the face with a hose, is quite

funny. The first place that large audiences saw the film was in a café in Paris. Amazed by the

images _____ on the white sheet, people lined up and waited for hours to see the
              4.

10-minute film. The Lumière brothers quickly became the men _____ the world
                                                                      5.

turned its attention. The brothers sent movie photographers around the world, all of whom were

told to film exotic locations, because people wanted to see moving pictures of these faraway

lands. The movies _____ were made did not have any sound, however. Sound was
                          6.

added in the late 1920s.

*B. Reread the radio broadcast. Then read each statement and circle **T** (true) or **F** (false).*

T **F**   0. The Lumière brothers invented the first working movie camera.

T **F**   1. The Lumière brothers made great contributions to film by inventing the first working movie camera.

T **F**   2. The first movie made with the expensive prototype was directed by the Lumière brothers themselves.

T **F**   3. In the first movie they made, there was a scene of workers, who worked in the same factory as the brothers, getting off work and leaving the factory at the end of the day.

T **F**   4. Their father's gardener, whom another part of the film featured, was sprayed in the face with a hose.

T **F**   5. The film was shown to large audiences in a café in Paris and it won first place.

T **F**   6. All of the brothers were sent around the world to film exotic places, because people wanted to see moving pictures of these faraway lands.

2 | ADVANCES OF VIDEO TECHNOLOGY

Read the statements from an article about the advances of video technology. Circle the correct choice in each sentence. (Circle the — if the sentence does not need to be corrected.)

0. The Lumière brothers would undoubtedly be amazed by the advances (resulting / which resulting) from their first movie camera.

1. The television camera, (which / that) was invented in the late 1920s, uses many of the same principles of recording as the first movie camera did.

2. There was a time (when / which) television cameras were as big as refrigerators.

3. The film (that used / used) by early television cameras was two inches wide.

4. The film (when / that) the producers used was not very sensitive, so the subjects needed lots of light.

5. People (— / who) were being filmed got hot very quickly.

6. Editors cut the film with razor blades and used clear tape, (that / which) held the film together.

7. Ed Ackerley is the man (that / which) invented the home movie camera.

8. Ackerley, (whom / whose) experience was mostly as a television cameraman, wanted a camera that was smaller and more portable.

9. His co-workers, (few of which / few of whom) thought it was possible to create a smaller

movie camera, were not very supportive of Ackerley's efforts.

10. Ackerley knew how to build his movie camera, but he did not have the money for the needed

materials, (most of which / most of whom) were very expensive.

11. Finally, Ackerley found a company (who / that) manufactured electronic equipment.

12. The company liked the ideas (of which / —) Ackerley presented.

13. Ackerley was the man (the company was looking for / for which the company was looking).

14. It was at this company (at which / where) home movie cameras were finally mass produced.

15. Ackerley, (that / whom) the company hired full time, continued to make many advances in

movie technology.

16. The improvements (— / of which) made in movies have made filmmaking available to almost

anyone.

17. Today's home movie cameras, (which calls / called) video cameras, feature a little screen that

shows the image you are filming and are more lightweight than the older cameras.

18. Despite the availability of inexpensive video cameras, most of the movies (playing / that

plays) in theaters are still very expensive to produce.

3 | WHAT MAKES YOU HAPPY?

A. *Read the following sentences from the first part of a magazine article about happiness.*
Rewrite the adjective clauses in parentheses as adjective phrases.

0. Recent studies (that were conducted) _____*conducted*_____ on happiness indicate

   that a number of factors contribute to how we feel.

1. One important factor (which contributes) _____ to our happiness is

   the opportunity for social interaction with family, friends, and acquaintances.

2. Part of this interaction often involves humor. It turns out that humor and laughing with

   others allow people to look at situations in a less serious way, (which makes)

   _____ negative events less stressful.

3. Social interaction allows us to build relationships. And these relationships provide support,

   (which includes) _____ companionship in recreational activities and

   physical help when needed.

4. Another factor (that was found) _____ to affect our happiness is

   work.

5. In many jobs, workers must reach goals (that have been set) _____

   by their bosses.

6. Goals that are too high result in workers (who are feeling) _____

   frustrated.

7. Goals that are just right result in workers (who are experiencing)

   _____ job satisfaction and overall happiness.

8. The last factor (that influences) _____ our happiness is our leisure

   activities.

9. Many people plan leisure activities (which involve) _____ other

   family members and friends.

10. These activities, then, provide opportunities for socializing, (which creates)

    _____ stronger relationships with family and friends and an

    increased level of happiness.

B. *Read the second part of the magazine article about happiness. Complete each sentence with a relative pronoun from the box. Some relative pronouns may be used more than once. (Note: There can be more than one correct answer.)*

| that | when | where | which | who | whom | whose |

Many other factors _____*that*_____ have been studied for their influence on happiness
0.

have resulted in interesting findings. For example, research done on money and happiness,

_____ origins go back many years, has revealed contradictory results. Lottery
1.

winners, some of _____ have been affected very negatively by their winnings, are
2.

generally no happier than the middle class. On the other hand, those _____ are
3.

very poor are less happy.

Music also affects how we feel. Researchers _____ work has focused on this
4.

area have found that listening to music, _____ is something completely under our
5.

control, can increase or decrease our happiness.

Psychologists _____ study happiness are interested in which personality traits
6.

are those of the happiest people. Extroversion, a personality trait _____ is
7.

characteristic of outgoing and friendly people, is highly related to happiness. Introversion,

expressed in antisocial behavior, can lead to depression, _____ is the opposite of
8.

happiness.

Happiness levels reported over the past several decades have not increased, even in countries

_____ the levels of prosperity have been rising. On an individual basis, a person's
9.

older years are generally a time _____ people are happiest.
10.

So, what can we do to be happier? What does all this research mean for us? Well, we can

read and think about the findings from the studies on happiness, _____ have been
11.

conducted over many years, look at our personal situations, and try to take some action to

become happier.

4 | EDITING: WILL MOVIE THEATERS GO DIGITAL?

Read the paragraph about digital movie theaters. There are ten mistakes in the use of adjective clauses. The first mistake is already corrected. Find and correct nine more. (Note: There can be more than one way to correct a mistake.)

  The technology of cinema, ~~that~~ *which* has made many advances over the years, could be headed for a digital future. It's likely that at least one major film whom you have seen recently was filmed digitally. You probably noticed, however, that the film did not look very good. Digital films do not look good when played in regular theaters, none which have digital screen projectors. This is because the digital film has to be transferred onto film what is used to project regular movies. As a result, the images projected onto the screen appeared fuzzy and washed-out. The problem is that digital projectors are extremely expensive, sold for eight to ten times the price of regular projectors. The theaters where have digital projectors could show their films with higher image quality. However, theater owners, most of whom make their money from drinks and popcorn, not from ticket sales, would not directly benefit from replacing their current projectors with digital ones. The companies that they distribute the films, however, would benefit from digital distribution because it is less expensive. The films that a company distributes digitally would also arrive at the theaters faster. Only time will tell whether the theaters we watch movies will show their films in high-quality digital, or continue as they have done for decades.

Unit 11 Achievement Test

30 Items
Score: _____

1 | LISTENING: THE HISTORY OF CHOCOLATE

🎧 **A.** *Listen to this story about the history of chocolate. Complete the story by writing the word(s) that you hear. You will hear the recording two times.*

Chocolate is a food _____*that*_____ is known and loved around the world. The Aztecs
            0.

are the ones _____ first enjoyed chocolate, which they drank with chili. They
               1.

shared their enthusiasm for the "drink of the gods" with Spanish explorers, _____
                                                                             2.

they met in the 16th century. It is believed that Queen Isabella of Spain first tasted chocolate

when she was feeling depressed. The chocolate, which has antidepressant qualities, seemed to lift

her mood immediately. The chocolate that Europeans drank did not contain chili but did contain

sugar, _____ counteracted the bitterness of the beverage. A new, profitable market
        3.

for the product grew among European nobility, _____ appetite for the chocolate
                                                4.

beverage was widespread by the 17th century. Most of the chocolate _____ is
                                                                     5.

consumed today is not drunk, but eaten, thanks to a chocolatier in England, who produced the

first solid chocolate in the mid-19th century. The chocolate bars _____ he
                                                                   6.

produced became so popular that he became the wealthiest man in England, next to the king.

The chocolate you see today is made much the same way as it was then.

B. Look at these sentences based on the story in Part A. Which of the two sentences is closest in meaning to the original sentence? Choose the correct answer.

__b__ 0. Chocolate is a food that is known and loved around the world.
     a. A food is known and loved around the world.
     b. As a food, chocolate is known and loved around the world.

_____ 1. The chocolate, which has antidepressant qualities, seemed to lift her mood immediately.
     a. Chocolate lifted her mood immediately.
     b. Chocolate did not lift her mood but an antidepressant did.

_____ 2. The chocolate that Europeans drank did not contain chili but did contain sugar.
     a. Europeans drank chocolate with chili.
     b. Europeans drank chocolate with sugar.

_____ 3. Most of the chocolate consumed today is not drunk, but eaten, thanks to a chocolatier in England, who produced the first solid chocolate in the mid-19th century.
     a. The first solid chocolate produced in England made it possible to eat chocolate.
     b. Consumers today drink more chocolate than eat it.

_____ 4. The chocolate you see today is made much the same way as it was then.
     a. There have been a lot of changes in the way chocolate is made.
     b. Today's chocolate is not very different from the chocolate people had in the past.

_____ 5. The chocolate bars produced by a chocolatier in England became so popular that he became the wealthiest man in England, next to the king.
     a. A chocolatier in England produced chocolate bars, which became very popular.
     b. The king of England was the person who produced the first solid chocolate.

_____ 6. The Aztecs are the ones who first enjoyed chocolate, which they drank with chili.
     a. The people who first enjoyed chocolate were the Aztecs, who drank it with chili.
     b. The Aztecs drank chocolate with chili when they first had it.

---

2 | DIFFERENT KINDS OF CHOCOLATE

Read the statements from an article about different kinds of chocolate. Circle the correct relative pronoun in each sentence. (Circle the — if no pronoun is needed.)

0. I come from a family ((that) / who) loves chocolate.

1. My two sisters always bake chocolate chip cookies, (which / that) are hard to resist.

2. However, my mom is the one (which / who) loves chocolate the most.

3. She's the one (that / which) makes chocolate cheesecake.

4. She has a recipe (where / whose) ingredients are a secret to all.

5. The chocolate (whom / —) you see most in the United States is milk chocolate.

6. However, the kind (that / when) I like best is dark chocolate.

7. White chocolate, (that / which) is made from cocoa butter, is my brother's favorite.

8. I didn't like it the first time (which / —) I tried it.

9. Our motto is, "The family (— / that) eats chocolate together stays together."

---

3 | CHOCOLATE AND YOUR HEALTH

Read this magazine article about chocolate and health. Complete the article. Use one of the pronouns and the correct form of the verb in parentheses.

There are many people _____*who have proclaimed*_____ the health benefits of
                              0. (who / whom) proclaim
chocolate over the years, but is chocolate really good for your health? It was the early 1990s

_____ to seek answers to that question, and you may be
1. (which / when) scientists / seriously begin
surprised by what they found. One study found that chocolate contains antioxidants, substances

which can prevent cancer. However, the person _____ milk
                                                2. (that / which) prefer
chocolate may not gain the same benefits, since the calcium in milk can block the absorption of

antioxidants. Chocolate also contains vitamins _____.
                                                3. (which / where) the body / need
However, the vitamins _____ can be found in other foods
                      4. (whom / that) chocolate / contain
_____ nearly as much fat or sugar. Although there is no doubt
5. (where / which) not contain
that chocolate tastes good, the benefits _____ for chocolate
                                         6. (that / what) many / claim
should be treated with caution.

---

4 | EDITING: WHICH HAS MORE CAFFEINE, COFFEE OR CHOCOLATE?

Read the letter to a health advice columnist and his response. There are four mistakes in the use of adjective clauses. The first mistake is already corrected. Find and correct three more. (Note: There can be more than one way to correct a mistake.)

Q: Dear Mr. Guy Health:

                  which
   I know that coffee, ~~that~~ I usually drink after dinner, has caffeine, but what about chocolate?

   The other night, I was at a café where has great coffee and chocolate, and I had both. I don't

   usually have trouble falling asleep, but I did that night. My question is, which has more

   caffeine, coffee or chocolate?

A: Coffee can contain 18 times more caffeine than a one-ounce milk chocolate bar. Caffeine is

   the chemical stimulant that beverages such as coffee and tea contain. It is also the chemical

   which it can keep you awake. On the other hand, chocolate has a lot of sugar, who often

   has a stimulating effect on the body. So if you're having trouble getting to sleep, avoid them

   both.

Unit 12 Achievement Test

30 Items
Score: _____

1 | LISTENING: COMMUNICATION WORKSHOP

🎧 **A.** *Listen to this radio ad for a communication workshop. Complete the ad by writing the word(s) that you hear. You will hear the recording two times.*

There is a problem _____*plaguing*_____ marriages today. The problem to which I'm referring
  0.

is poor communication between husbands and wives. Disagreements between couples, cases of

which will occur even in the best of marriages, can be resolved through effective communication

skills. Couples _____ to improve their communication are invited to the Marriage
               1.

and Communication Workshop. This three-day workshop, _____ Dr. Reese
                                                      2.

Sinclair, will help you learn the skills necessary for a peaceful, loving marriage. This is the

workshop that couples have been raving about. The skills _____ in the workshop
                                                         3.

will change your marriage for the better. You will learn how everyone who wants to feel

appreciated will respond to both verbal and nonverbal signs of acceptance. You will also learn

the seven secrets of understanding the person you are talking _____. In addition,
                                                              4.

you will receive invaluable books written by Dr. Sinclair that are not sold in bookstores. The

ideas _____ in the books will serve as your reference long after the workshop is
      5.

over. This is the opportunity you've been waiting for. Reserve your seats for the workshop,

_____ at the Central Library, by calling now, or log on to www.centrallibrary.com.
  6.

B. *Look at the following sentences from the radio ad in Exercise A. Which of the two sentences is closest in meaning to the original sentence? Choose the correct answer.*

___*a*___ 0. There is a problem plaguing marriages today.

    a. A problem is plaguing marriages today.

    b. A problem which is plaguing marriages today.

_____ 1. The problem to which I'm referring is poor communication between husbands and wives.

    a. I'm referring to the problem which is between husbands and wives.

    b. Poor communication between husbands and wives is the problem I'm talking about.

_____ 2. Disagreements between couples, cases of which will occur even in the best of marriages, can be resolved through effective communication skills.

    a. Disagreements can occur even in the best marriages.

    b. Disagreements between couples in the best marriages can be resolved through effective communication skills.

_____ 3. This is the workshop that couples have been raving about.

    a. Those couples have been raving about this workshop.

    b. Couples have been raving about the workshop.

_____ 4. You will learn how everyone who wants to feel appreciated will respond to both verbal and nonverbal signs of acceptance.

    a. You are one of those who want to feel appreciated, and you will learn how to respond to verbal and nonverbal signs of acceptance.

    b. People who want to feel appreciated will show you how to respond to verbal and nonverbal signs of acceptance.

_____ 5. In addition, you will receive invaluable books written by Dr. Sinclair that are not sold in bookstores.

    a. You won't be able to find these books which are written by Dr. Sinclair because they are not sold in bookstores.

    b. The author of the books, Dr. Sinclair, will give you his books as a free gift.

_____ 6. This is the opportunity you've been waiting for.

    a. You've been waiting for this kind of opportunity.

    b. You have the opportunity to wait for this.

PART IV

2 | TALK OF LOVE

Read the statements from a passage on the topic of love. Complete each sentence with an adjective clause using the quantifier in parentheses + a preposition + a relative pronoun.

0. My friend Keiko and I have wonderful conversations, _____*most of which*_____ are about

    <u>(most)</u>

    our boyfriends.

1. On the other hand, our boyfriends, _____ we love dearly, are simply

    <u>(both)</u>

    not the best conversational partners for us.

2. Yesterday, Keiko and I tried to think of ways to get our men to talk to us,

    _____ will work.

    <u>(none)</u>

3. We thought we could try to talk to them about sports, _____ I don't

    <u>(most)</u>

    even understand.

4. Keiko had the idea of e-mailing or sending instant messages to our boyfriends,

    _____ my boyfriend likes to do.

    <u>(neither)</u>

5. Keiko recommended that I look into some authors, _____ I had heard

    <u>(some)</u>

    of before.

6. These authors, _____ names I've forgotten now, have written about

    <u>(all)</u>

    communication between men and women.

3 | BOOK REVIEW

Read the following sentences from a review of the book You Talk, Me Listen. *Rewrite the adjective clauses in parentheses as adjective phrases.*

0. *You Talk, Me Listen,* a new book _____*written*_____ by Harvey Zaff, Ph.D.,
   (which was written)

   discusses the communication differences between men and women.

1. In the book, Zaff discusses studies _____ how men and women speak
   (that highlight)

   to each other, and why it often does not work.

2. One of the earliest studies _____ in 1972 found that women connect
   (which was published)

   through conversation, while men connect through doing things together.

3. Zaff, _____ a bit like Freud at times, argues that men communicate to
   (who sounds)

   establish superiority over others and to set themselves apart.

4. On the other hand, women, _____ to keep the peace, use
   (who try)

   communication to establish equality.

5. His many stories, _____ over 20 years of counseling, are particularly
   (which he compiled)

   useful.

6. *You Talk, Me Listen,* _____ this week, offers some interesting tips for
   (which was released)

   improving communication between the sexes.

4	**EDITING: COMMUNICATION AT WORK**

Read the paragraph about communication at work. There are seven mistakes in the use of adjective clauses. The first mistake is already corrected. Find and correct six more. (Note: There is often more than one way to correct a mistake.)

                                                                   working

Around the world, one can find men and women, ~~work~~ in the same office together.

Communication differences between men and women, an example which is illustrated in the

following story, can cause problems at work. For example, a female supervisor, seek to

inform her male boss about a problem employee, may not want advice from her boss. The

boss, believes that she wants advice, begins telling her what to do with the employee, leaving

the woman feeling frustrated. In addition, some studies have found that ideas which

presented by women in meetings may receive little response, while a man who presents nearly

the same idea a few minutes later gets all the credit. Also, the female boss which

communication style is more like a man's is seen as having more authority. Meanwhile, the

male boss which we read about earlier could benefit by learning about how women's

communication style may differ from his own.

Part IV Achievement Test

1 | LISTENING: THE FIRST TELEPHONE

🎧 **A.** *Listen to this radio broadcast about the first telephone. Complete the passage by writing the word(s) that you hear. You will hear the recording two times.*

Many people _____*working*_____ separately contributed to the invention of the telephone.
 0.
The first working telephone is now credited to the Italian inventor _____ Antonio
 1.
Meucci. He demonstrated his telephone publicly in New York in 1850, an account of which was

written in an Italian-language newspaper. The telephone, _____ used electricity to
 2.
transmit sound across electric wires, was a breakthrough in communication. The most famous

first telephone call, made by Alexander Graham Bell, was to his assistant, Mr. Watson. Bell,

_____ just spilled some battery acid on himself, said "Mr. Watson, come here. I
 3.
want to see you!" The telephone that they built underwent some changes, _____
 4.
improvements in the volume. The first telephone system that existed was organized by Bell in

1877. The circular dial with numbers, developed 11 years later, allowed people to dial different

telephone numbers. Thomas Edison is another person _____ history owes some
 5.
credit for the telephone. He improved the mouthpiece on the phone so that sounds were clearer,

and it is the same style of mouthpiece _____ is still produced today. There are
 6.
many other people who helped to invent the telephone, all of whom have improved our ability to

communicate today.

*B. Reread the radio broadcast. Then read each statement and circle **T** (true) or **F** (false).*

T (F) 0. The telephone was invented solely by the Italian inventor Antonio Meucci.

T **F** 1. An article about Antonio Meucci's telephone demonstration in 1850 was published in an Italian-language newspaper.

T **F** 2. The first telephone call made by Alexander Graham Bell was to Antonio Meucci.

T **F** 3. The telephone Bell and his assistants built is the same style produced today.

T **F** 4. The first telephone system that existed was organized by Edison.

T **F** 5. The circular dial with numbers, that was developed 11 years later, allowed people to dial different telephone numbers.

T **F** 6. All of those who helped to invent the telephone have improved our ability to communicate today.

2 | EFFICIENCY

Read the statements from an article about working more efficiently. Circle the correct choice in each sentence. (Circle the — if the sentence does not need to be corrected.)

0. Many people feel like they don't have enough time, (resulting / which result) in frustration.

1. Why do people (who / which) work hard feel overworked and underproductive?

2. For most professionals, there was never a time in school (when / which) they were taught *how* to work efficiently.

3. Furthermore, many of the techniques (that used / used) to "save time" are actually time wasters.

4. This is because many of the routines (whose / that) professionals establish for work are not reevaluated when situations change.

5. People (— / who) are not ready to change to keep up with changing demands and situations will be at a disadvantage.

6. One efficiency tip is to organize your personal work space, (that / which) will reduce the time you spend looking for things.

7. Another tip (that / where) can save you time is to plan ahead.

8. Take Tom as an example of a professional (whom / whose) lack of planning was slowing him down.

9. During the day, Tom had many ideas about things he should do, (few of whom /

   few of which) he remembered because he did not write them down.

10. Tom began to write down the things that he needed to do, (most of which / most of whom)

    would not take very much time to do, but used to take lots of time to *remember* to do!

11. Tom would then organize his to-do list in a way (what / that) reflected the importance he

    assigned to each task.

12. Tom soon found himself accomplishing all of the things (of which / —) he wrote down.

13. Procrastination, or putting things off, is another time thief (that you should be aware of /

    of whom you should be aware).

14. Tom's office was a place (at which / where) Mr. Procrastination had come to live.

15. The time (— / of which) he let slip by made his work seem impossible to accomplish.

16. However, Tom, (who / from whom) his company expected a lot, decided to adopt an attitude

    of "do it now!"

17. Now, a paper (which cross / crossing) his desk does not stay there for long.

18. Tom deals with the paper, (filing / that files) it away when he's done.

3 | CELL PHONES AND PROBLEMS

A. *Read the magazine article about problems with cell phones and driving. Rewrite the adjective clauses in parentheses as adjective phrases.*

0. The cell phone is an invention _____*changing*_____ the way that people communicate.
   (that has changed)

1. However, there are some interesting new problems _____ by cell phones.
   (that have been created)

2. A topic _____ by many people is talking on cell phones while driving.
   (that is debated)

3. Although cell phones allow people to call 911 to report crimes easily while on the road, a

   major problem _____ to cell phones and driving is distraction.
   (that is related)

4. Cell phone use is one of many possible distractions _____ the driver from
   (that prevents)

   responding to traffic quickly.

5. In addition, drivers _____ on the phone may not hear sirens or other cars
   (who are talking)

   honking.

6. Many European countries, _____ to protect their citizens, require a "hands
   (which are attempting)

   free" system for cell phones.

7. In the United States, many states have banned the use of hand-held cell phones, and the police

   are the ones _____ responsible for enforcing the law.
   (who are held)

B. *Read the magazine article about camera phones. Complete each sentence with a relative pronoun from the box. Some relative pronouns may be used more than once. (Note: There can be more than one correct answer.)*

that	when	where	which	who	whom	whose

Camera phones are cell phones _____*that*_____ have photo and video capabilities. These
0.

advances in technology, _____ benefits many of us enjoy, also cause some
1.

problems. For example, camera phones are the devices to _____ many people
2.

credit identity theft. It is possible that the person behind you at the checkout counter may be

taking a picture of your credit card, _____ you may not notice. Camera phones,
3.

some of _____ are almost entirely silent, are sometimes hard to detect. Phones
4.

_____ are equipped with cameras can also steal information from copyrighted
5.

materials, especially charts, graphs, and photographs from books. This is a problem

_____ influence is affecting book sales in many bookstores. As a result, companies
6.

in South Korea _____ manufacture camera phones are required by law to make the
7.

camera phones beep when a picture is taken. Many students _____ have cell
8.

phones use them to send e-mails during class time. Teachers and professors, for

_____ this phenomenon is very disturbing, have openly expressed their concerns.
9.

Some schools have instituted cell-phone bans, _____ seems to have reduced this
10.

problem. Finally, cell phones, _____ radio waves are everywhere, may disturb the
11.

operation of pacemakers, which keep a person's heart beating. In some hospitals,

_____ there is much concern about cell phones interfering with medical equipment,
12.

cell phone use has been banned. Finally, there have been several cases _____ have
13.

been reported in the news of cell phones that have exploded or caught fire. Hopefully, there will

be a time in the near future _____ these problems will no longer be with us.
14.

4 | EDITING: THE FUTURE OF CELL PHONES

Read the paragraph about the future of cell phones. There are ten mistakes in the use of adjective clauses. The first mistake is already corrected. Find and correct nine more. (Note: There can be more than one way to correct a mistake.)

          which

The technology of the telephone, ~~that~~ has evolved since its invention, will most likely continue to change. A particular advance what you may have heard about is speech recognition. This technology is currently available, but not in cell phones, none which currently have enough memory to handle it. However, in the future, a voice message what you leave for someone could be transformed to text and sent as an e-mail. In addition, cell phones that produced in the future may include automatic speech translation into other languages. However, machine translation, require a great deal more development, may not be available for your cell phone very soon. One change that you may soon see is a cell phone where has the ability to store thousands of your favorite songs. Other possibilities, some of whom may never happen, require surgical procedures. One group of researchers that they want to take "hands free" to the limit is looking into implants that are placed in a tooth. The devices that a dentist implants surgically could both receive and send messages. Or maybe the cell phones when we talk on in the future will be a part of us from birth, created in our DNA. Our biggest problem may then be how to dial.

PART V Diagnostic Test

60 Items
Score: _____

🎧 **A.** *Listen to this introduction to a book about adoption. Complete the introduction by writing the word(s) that you hear. You will hear the recording two times.*

Adoption is a legal action that _____is taken_____ to create a parent-child
                                              0.

relationship between people who are not related by blood. There are several reasons why

children _____ for adoption. One is that the birth parents feel they are
                      1.

not prepared to care for their child. Another is that sometimes parents

_____ their parental rights due to abuse or neglect of their children.
          2.

And, in some cases, children are left alone because their parents have died.

When a child _____, he or she is regarded by law as being a full
                          3.

member of the adopted family and _____ to have all the same rights as a
                                              4.

biological child. This _____ that the adopted child should
                              5.

_____ the same love and care that a biological child is given.
          6.

Adoption laws _____ to be complex. The adoption process
                          7.

_____ by the fact that it _____ differently in
          8.   **9.**

each state and country. Some efforts _____ to standardize adoption laws.
                                              10.

However, it _____ that people wishing to adopt work with a lawyer
                      11.

specializing in adoption law.

The process can sometimes be long and frustrating, but with time and effort, adoptions can

_____ successfully.
          12.

PART V

B. Reread the introduction to the book. Then read each statement and circle **T** (true) or
F (false).

(T) F 0. Parents who wish to adopt a child should work with a lawyer specializing in
adoption law.

T F 1. Through adoption, a parent-child relationship can be created between people
who have no blood relationship.

T F 2. People often want to adopt because they feel that they are not ready to take
care of their own child.

T F 3. Some children are put up for adoption after the death of their parents.

T F 4. According to the law, adopted and biological children should have equal rights.

T F 5. The adoption process is usually clear and easy to follow because adoption laws
are regulated and standardized.

2 INTERNATIONAL ADOPTION

*Read this information from an adoption agency brochure. Complete the brochure with the
correct verb forms. Write the letter of the best answer on each line.*

Many children _____*a*_____ (a. are adopted b. are adopting c. have adopted d. adopted) by parents from
     0.

different countries. These adoptions _____ (a. have called b. are called c. had called d. were called)
     1.

international adoptions. Most international adoptions _____ (a. have arranged b. arranged c. are
     2.

arranged d. are arranging) by an adoption agency rather than by a lawyer. Nevertheless, it _____
     3.

(a. is still recommended b. still recommends c. was still recommended d. has still recommended) that the

adoption process _____ (a. guided b. was guided c. be guided d. has been guided) by a lawyer who
     4.

_____ (a. was specialized b. specializes c. be specialized d. has been specialized) in international
   5.

adoption.

One reason international adoption _____ (a. is thought b. thinks c. thought d. has thought) to
     6.

be complicated is because of the differences among countries in laws, culture, and language.

Parents adopting from abroad usually need to _____ (a. have translated documents b. translate
     7.

documents c. have documents translated d. have documents translate) by an interpreter who _____
     8.

(a. has approved b. be approved c. approved d. is approved) to translate official documents. Another

concern is the expensive and last-minute travel that is often required.

So why do some people prefer international adoptions in spite of the many challenges that

_____ (a. associate b. have associated c. associated d. are associated) with it? Some parents _____
  9.   **10.**

(a. are preferred b. prefer c. were preferred d. have been preferred) international adoption because contact

with the birth parents _____ (a. are considered b. have considered c. is considered d. has considered)
                                 11.

less likely.

Domestic adoption, on the other hand, _____ (a. regards b. regarded c. has regarded d. is
                                               12.

regarded) by many adoptive parents as less complicated. If the child _____ (a. located b. locates
                                                              13.

c. is located d. has located) in the region where the adoptive parents live, considerable expenses

_____ (a. be avoided b. can be avoided c. have avoided d. would have been avoided). The information
  14.

that _____ (a. is provided b. provided c. is providing d. has provided) about the child won't have to
     15.

be translated. If any paperwork _____ (a. did not complete b. has not completed c. has not been
                                                16.

completed d. was not been completed) correctly, the adoptive parents can _____ (a. have it taken care
                                                                17.

of b. have it take care of c. have taken care of it d. taken care of it) more easily.

PART V

3 | ADJUSTING TO A NEW FAMILY

Read this pamphlet about changes in an adoptive family. Complete the pamphlet by writing the correct forms of the verbs. Some items may have more than one correct answer.

A family's period of emotional adjustment after an adoption

_____*is affected*_____ by many factors, such as the age and background of the
      0. (affect)

adopted child. Parents who _____ to adopt should
              1. (plan)

_____ about what to expect when their
    2. (inform)

child comes to live with them. The emotions a parent experiences at that time

_____ of conflicting feelings. It _____
    3. (often make up)   **4. (assume)**

by many parents that they will instantly bond with their child. However, it is common for

parents who adopt an older child _____ by him or her at the
              5. (reject)

beginning. It _____ that this _____
    6. (think)   **7. (connect)**

with feelings of insecurity that the child might have. The behavior should

_____ as normal.
    8. (regard)

    Adopted children _____ for the changes involved in becoming
          9. (sometimes not prepare)

part of a new family. Even if children are old enough to understand what adoption is, they

_____ about their adoption until a day or two before it happens. In
    10. (generally not tell)

addition, children who _____ in a facility forchildren without
         11. (institutionalize)

parents _____ to be immature for their age. Also, if the child that
    12. (often find)

_____ is of a different race than the parents, he or she
    13. (adopt)

_____ by others as different, causing the child to feel uneasy about
    14. (often judge)

his or her family ties. All of these issues should _____ as normal.
              15. (think of)

    With time, as the child _____ that he or she is a full part of the
          16. (feel)

family, many of these problems can _____.
          17. (overcome)

4 | EDITING: AN ADOPTION STORY

Read this e-mail about one woman's experience with adoption. There are ten mistakes in the use of verb forms. The first mistake is already corrected. Find and correct nine more. (Note: There may be more than one way to correct a mistake.)

Hi Mark,

How have you been? It's been a really busy year for Jim and me. As you know, we ~~are~~ *were/got*
married last spring. We knew that we wanted to adopt a child from abroad, so we got started
on the process right away. We filled out a lot of forms and had them checking by our
attorney. We were interview by the adoption agency. A few months later it was finally
happened—we got approve by Adoptions International. We were told that our new son was
waiting for us in Russia. There was so much to do! We had travel plans making by a travel
agent. We learned some phrases that had translated by a Russian friend. And of course we
fixed up the house for the arrival of our new son. We got his room painting and had it
decorating especially for him. We want him to know that he considered a very important part
of our family. I'm excited for you to meet him. I'll call you when I get a chance.

Love,

Emily

Unit 13 Achievement Test

30 Items
Score: _____

1 | LISTENING: SEAT BELTS

🎧 **A.** *Listen to this public service announcement about wearing seat belts. Complete the announcement by writing the word(s) that you hear. You will hear the recording two times.*

When you're in a hurry, the last thing that you want to think about is safety precautions that take extra time. But the second that it takes to put on a seat belt could give you extra years of life. Just ask Doug Banhar.

Doug _____was asked_____ to be at work early one morning. He was in a hurry when he left
0.
the house, but he took a second to make sure that his seat belt _____ before he
1.
started driving. It's a good thing he did, because that second saved his life. As he was driving, an animal suddenly ran into the road. He swerved to avoid the animal, but he hit a tree. Because Doug's seat belt was on, he did not _____ badly. Only his leg and hand were cut.
2.
He _____ to the hospital, where he was examined and released. Thanks to his seat
3.
belt, Doug was given a second chance at life. Without it, he could have been thrown from the car.

So what's your excuse for not wearing a seat belt? They're uncomfortable? Today's seat belts
_____ to be more comfortable than they used to be. You're a good driver? Even if
4.
you consider yourself a good driver, you may still _____ by a bad driver. You just
5.
don't want to? Wearing a seat belt is required by law. And most importantly, seat belts can save your life.

B. *Reread the public service announcement. Then read each statement and circle **T** (true) or **F** (false).*

T **(F)** 0. Doug Banhar asked a few people to go to work early with him.

T **F** 1. Doug was not seriously hurt because he had his seat belt on.

T **F** 2. Doug drove himself to the hospital.

T **F** 3. Doug was thrown from the car when he got into the car accident.

T **F** 4. Doug was hit by a bad driver.

T **F** 5. Drivers have to wear a seat belt according to the law.

2 | FOOD SAFETY

Read this magazine article about food safety. Circle the correct verb form in each sentence.

Thousands of people 0. (are affected)/ affected) by food poisoning every year. Fortunately,

your chances of getting food poisoning 1. (can be reduced / can reduce) by taking some

simple precautions. First, always make sure you wash your hands before touching any food.

Bacteria 2. (are spread / are spreading) around the kitchen quickly if you do not keep your

hands clean. Second, all types of meat should 3. (cook / be cooked) thoroughly before being

eaten. Most cases of food poisoning 4. (caused / are caused) by undercooked meat. Third,

refrigerate your food. Bacteria growth 5. (is being slowed / is slowed) by cold temperatures,

so bacteria will not have time to grow if food 6. (is refrigerated / refrigerates) immediately.

Finally, food that 7. (left / is left) in the refrigerator for more than a few days should be

discarded.

3 | JOB PROMOTION

Read Nancy's diary entry about her promotion. Complete the diary entry by writing the correct form of each verb. Some items may have more than one correct answer.

Dear Diary,

What an eventful day! When I arrived at work today, I _____ was told _____

0. (tell)

that my supervisor wanted to talk to me. Well, I found out I've _____! A

1. (promote)

little celebration _____ in my honor during lunch. This promotion comes

2. (hold)

at a good time; I was starting to _____ because I thought that my hard

3. (frustrate)

work wasn't appreciated. But I guess now I'm _____ for all that hard

4. (reward)

work, and it sure feels good. I'm glad I never _____! After work I was in

5. (complain)

such a good mood that I got my hair _____, and I got my nails

6. (do)

_____. Then I had my car _____, and I'm

7. (manicure)   8. (wash

having my clothes _____. I guess I just want to look as good as I feel!

9. (dry-clean)

PART V

4 | EDITING: ROCK SLIDE

Read this news story. There are five mistakes in the use of verb forms. The first mistake is already corrected. Find and correct four more. (Note: There can be more than one way to correct a mistake.)

                   was injured

A motorist ~~injured~~ when a rock slide fell onto Canyon Highway late this morning. Aaron Weil was on his way to Harrison Park where his son getting marry. Emergency medical technicians arrived to find that Weil's car trapped under the rocks, but miraculously Weil was survived and is in critical but stable condition. He is being hold overnight at a local hospital for observation.

Unit 14 Achievement Test

| 1 | **LISTENING: ASTEROIDS, A POTENTIAL THREAT?** |

🎧 **A.** *Listen to this paragraph about asteroids. Complete the paragraph by writing the word(s) that you hear. You will hear the recording two times.*

An asteroid _____*is defined*_____ as a rock that circles, or orbits, the sun. Asteroids
                              0.

and planets _____: Both follow regular orbits around the sun, but
                          1.

asteroids are much smaller than planets. Most of the asteroids that _____
                                                                              2.

in our solar system are located between Mars and Jupiter. But there _____
                                                                              3.

to be thousands more that we haven't yet discovered. Most asteroids are quite small and not

_____ dangerous by scientists, but there are some which
            4.

_____ to be potential threats to Earth. As a result, telescopes with
            5.

computers have _____ to detect asteroids that could collide with the
                          6.

Earth.

B. *Reread the paragraph about asteroids. Then read each statement and circle* **T** *(true) or* **F** *(false).*

Ⓣ **F**   0. An asteroid is a rock that circles the sun.

T **F**   1. Most asteroids in our solar system are found between Mars and Jupiter.

T **F**   2. Scientists think that small asteroids are dangerous.

T **F**   3. Scientists can use telescopes with computers to detect asteroids that could
             collide with the Earth.

2 | BLACK HOLES

Read this excerpt from a science article about black holes. Circle the correct verb form in each sentence.

A black hole is an area in outer space into which everything near it is pulled and

0. (is never seen / never be seen) again. Black holes **1.** (are thought that / are thought to have)

such strong gravity that even light cannot escape their pull.

In science fiction, black holes **2.** (are sometimes regarded / are sometimes regarding) as

mysterious things. They've even been described as doors to another universe. In reality,

however, they **3.** (are said that / are said to be) what is left after the death of a giant star.

Many black holes **4.** (have been found as / have been found in) the universe. They

5. (are divided into / divide into) two kinds: regular and supermassive, or extra big. Black

holes **6.** (consider as / are considered to be) the largest sources of energy in the universe. It

7. (is thought that / is thought to be) black holes are at the center of most galaxies, including

our own.

3 | THE NORTHERN LIGHTS

Read this article from the Internet about the northern lights. Complete the article by writing the correct form of each verb. Some items may have more than one correct answer.

The northern lights, or Aurora Borealis, are the colorful, moving lights that

_____are sometimes seen_____ in the sky in the northern hemisphere. In the past, different
      0. (sometimes see)

groups of people had a variety of ideas about what the lights meant. In some cultures, it

_____ that the lights were the souls of animals dancing. The lights
      1. (assume)

_____ by others to be the spirits of unmarried women who had died. In
      2. (believe)

other cultures, the lights _____ to come from a volcano that
      3. (think)

_____ in the north by ancestors to provide light and warmth in those
      4. (place)

dark lands. Despite their differences, the interpretations _____ by a clear
      5. (all connect)

sense of awe that people felt when they saw the northern lights.

Today the northern lights _____ as one of nature's most beautiful
      6. (regard)

natural phenomena. Most often, the colorful displays _____ of white,
      7. (make up)

green, and yellow lights. But blue, violet, pink, and red lights have also been witnessed.

It _____ that the northern lights occur when storms on the surface of
      8. (believe)

the sun affect the atmosphere of the Earth. The colors of the lights depend on the atoms that

_____ in the atmosphere.
      9. (find)

4 | EDITING: LIFE ON MARS

Read this article about life on Mars. There are six mistakes in the use of verb forms. The first mistake is already corrected. Find and correct five more.

                                               was

Before the age of space exploration, Mars considered to be a possible home for
                                                    ^

intelligent life. Stories about life on Mars have long made up to scare and entertain us.

Although Martians are no longer thought exist, it believes that the planet supported some

forms of life millions of years ago. Fossils that find in a meteorite on Mars are regarded to be

strong evidence that bacteria may have inhabited the planet at one time.

Part V Achievement Test

1 | LISTENING: ORGANIC FARMING

🎧 *A.* *Listen to this information about organic farming. Complete the information by writing the word(s) that you hear. You will hear the recording two times.*

Organic farming refers to a method of farming in which no chemicals or pesticides

_____*are used*_____ to grow plants or raise animals. It _____
　　　　　　0.　　　　　　　　　　　　　　　　　　　　　　　　**1.**

by some people to be an environmentally friendly way to farm. Land doesn't

_____ by chemicals when food is raised organically. Also, it
　　　　　2.

_____ that people are less likely to _____ from
　　　　　3.　　　　　　　　　　　　　　　　　　　　**4.**

organic food than from food that is grown conventionally.

So why are chemicals and pesticides used if they're not good for the land or for us? The main

reason is that fruits and vegetables that _____ with pesticides are less
　　　　　　　　　　　　　　　　　　　　　　5.

likely to be eaten by insects; therefore, production is greatly increased. This

_____ that more food _____ available at a lower
　　　　　6.　　　　　　　　　　　　　　　　　　**7.**

cost. For this reason, the use of chemicals and pesticides _____ by many
　　　　　　　　　　　　　　　　　　　　　　　　　　　　8.

as a way to improve standards of living, especially in developing countries.

Special caution _____ when choosing fresh food for children, whose
　　　　　　　　　　　9.

tolerance levels for chemicals are believed to be much lower than those of adults. The chemicals

_____ some foods may make children sick. It is recommended that only
　　　　10.

foods that _____ organically be given to children until they weigh at
　　　　　　　11.

least 70 pounds, or 32 kilograms. This recommendation is fairly easy to follow, as many organic

products _____ in regular grocery stores.
　　　　　12.

B. *Reread the information about organic farming. Then read each statement and circle* **T** *(true) or* **F** *(false).*

Ⓣ   **F**   **0.** Some people believe that organic farming is an environmentally friendly way to farm.

T   **F**   **1.** Farmers who adopt organic farming methods do not use chemicals or pesticides when growing fruits and vegetables or when raising animals.

T   **F**   **2.** There is no reason for chemicals and pesticides to be used.

T   **F**   **3.** Insects can reduce production by eating fruits and vegetables on which no chemicals or pesticides are used.

T   **F**   **4.** It is recommended that children be fed organic foods because chemicals in foods can harm them.

T   **F**   **5.** It is believed that adults and children have different tolerance levels for chemicals.

2 | VEGETARIANISM

Read this information from a pamphlet at a natural foods store. Complete the pamphlet with the correct verb forms. Write the letter of the best answer on each line.

Vegetarianism is a dietary practice that ____*a*____ **(a. is embraced b. embraced c. has embraced**
                                        0.

d. was embraced) by many people around the world. Vegetarians _____ **(a. often divide b. are often**
                                                                1.

divided c. often divided d. have often divided) into two categories: those who eat eggs, milk, and cheese,

and those who do not. Those who do not _____ **(a. known as b. have known as c. are known as**
                                         2.

d. know as) vegans.

Many vegetarians _____ **(a. have chosen b. have been chosen c. were chosen d. are chosen)** their
                 3.

meat-free lifestyles for health, environmental, or ethical reasons. The health benefits of

vegetarianism _____ **(a. have been well documented b. have well documented c. documented well d. have**
              4.

documented well). Vegetarians are less likely to _____ **(a. affect b. have affected c. be affected d. have**
                                                   5.

been affected) by cancer or heart disease than meat eaters. People _____ **(a. have shown b. showed**
                                                                      6.

c. show d. have been shown) to lose weight when they begin a vegetarian diet. (However, as with any

diet, it _____ **(a. recommends b. has recommended c. recommended d. is recommended)** that the dieter
         7.

have his or her weight loss _____ **(a. to be monitored b. monitored c. monitor d. monitoring)** by a
                            8.

physician.) Many vegetarians argue that large amounts of land and water _____ **(a. are needed**
                                                                        9.

b. have been needed c. needed d. have needed) to raise animals for food, whereas far smaller amounts

of resources _____ (a. required b. have been required c. are required d. require) to grow grains, fruits,
          10.

and vegetables. In addition, some of the common practices that _____ (a. involved b. involve
                                                                  11.

c. are involved d. have involved) in raising animals are believed by many vegetarians to be unethical.

For instance, many animals _____ (a. have given b. are given c. gave d. were given) steroids to
                         12.

enhance their growth or increase their production of eggs or milk. This practice _____
                                                                              13.

(a. is considered b. considered c. have considered d. is considering) normal by many consumers, but it may

_____ (a. be motivating b. motivate c. be motivated d. have motivated) by money, with little regard
     14.

for the effects on people's health.

Some people who follow a vegetarian diet _____ (a. encourage b. are encouraged c. are
                                              15.

encouraging d. have encouraged) to do so for religious reasons. These people _____ (a. are followed
                                                                          16.

b. have been followed c. were followed d. follow) religions that teach that all animal life should

_____ (a. have regarded b. regard c. have been regarded d. be regarded) as sacred. They don't believe
     17.

in using animals for food.

3 | RECYCLING AND REUSING

Read these paragraphs from an Internet website about recycling and reusing. Complete the paragraphs by writing the correct form of each verb.

Recycling is the process of reusing materials that may _____<u>be assumed</u>_____
0. (assume)

to be waste. Collection containers _____ in many cities and
1. (locate)

towns around the world, where people can put cardboard, glass, metal, paper, or plastic to

_____. These items _____
2. (recycle)   **3. (pick up)**

and taken away. Then the materials _____ to produce other
4. (use)

products. Right now you _____ by products that
5. (probably surround)

_____ of recycled materials.
6. (make up)

  Instead of _____ and produced again, however, many items
7. (destroy)

can simply _____. For instance, many books that
8. (reuse)

_____ in cafés, bookstores, or libraries once
9. (find)

_____ to someone else. One restaurant owner in our
10. (belong)

town keeps her coffee grounds instead of throwing them away. Later they

_____ by local school children who use them in place of
11. (collect)

fertilizer in their school vegetable garden. The children sell their vegetables to the same

restaurant, where they _____ to make fresh salads and
12. (cut up)

sandwiches. The food there _____ to be the tastiest in town.
13. (think)

  Reusing and recycling _____ to be two of the best ways to
14. (believe)

reduce waste and to save natural resources. Reusing _____
15. (consider)

preferable to recycling, if possible. It _____ that one man's
16. (often say)

garbage _____ as another man's treasure. Who ever thought
17. (regard)

that this saying could help save the environment, too!

4 | EDITING: HOME REPAIRS

Read this paragraph from Dan's journal about the repairs he's planning to make on his house. There are ten mistakes in the use of verb forms. The first mistake is already corrected. Find and correct nine more. (Note: There may be more than one way to correct a mistake.)

     Rosa and I bought our first house today! We offered the sellers a fair price, and our

           was

offer ∧ accepted! It's an older home, and there are a lot of repairs that need to do. I guess the

house considered a "fixer upper." We can't be afforded to have all of the repairs make right

now, but we want to start on a few projects. First I want to get the roof fix. It leaks when it

rains, so of course I need to have the ceiling repair as well. Then I'll have the plumbing

replace. After those big things are done, we can have the carpets clean and get the walls paint

and we can move in. We can hardly wait!

PART VI Diagnostic Test

1 | LISTENING: SURVIVAL

🎧 **A.** *Listen and complete this advertisement for an upcoming TV show by writing the word(s) that you hear. You will hear the recording two times.*

Coming this week on *Survival:* Animals are able _____*to defend*_____ themselves
                                                                    0.

in some amazing ways. Animals continue _____ because they are
                                                          1.

naturally equipped to protect themselves. Humans are not. Without weapons, it probably would

have been impossible for humans _____ to this day. First, humans had
                                                     2.

sticks and stones; then they went on _____ gun powder, then nuclear
                                                        3.

bombs. You'll be amazed _____ the awe-inspiring ways in which
                                          4.

animals—and humans—defend themselves. You won't want _____ it,
                                                                              5.

this week on *Survival.*

B. *Reread the advertisement. Then read each statement and circle* **T** *(true) or* **F** *(false).*

T **Ⓕ** **0.** "Animals are able to defend themselves" means the same as "Animals are able
          defending themselves."

T **F** **1.** "Animals continue to survive" means the same as "Animals continue
          surviving."

T **F** **2.** "Humans went on to make gun powder" means the same as "Humans went on
          making gun powder."

C. *Read these sentences based on the advertisement in Exercise A. Write* **S** *if the infinitive is used as a subject,* **O** *if it is used as an object, or* **SC** *if it is used as a subject complement.*

___*O*___ **0.** Animals are able <u>to defend</u> themselves.

_____ **1.** One of animals' instincts is <u>to protect</u> themselves.

_____ **2.** <u>To survive</u> without weapons probably would have been impossible for humans.

_____ **3.** Everyone will want <u>to watch</u> *Survival.*

2 | ANIMAL DEFENSE

Read this paragraph from a biology textbook about how animals defend themselves.
Complete the paragraph with the correct verb forms. Write the best answer on each line.

Some common ways for animals ____*a*____ (a. to defend b. defend c. defending d. to have defended)
0.

themselves are hibernation, camouflage, mimicry, and migration. _____ (a. Hibernate b. To be
1.

hibernating c. Hibernating d. To hibernate), or sleeping through the winter, is one way some animals

defend themselves against starvation. These animals spend the warm months _____
2.

(a. to gather b. to have gathered c. gathering d. having gathered) food, and survive the cold months by

_____ (a. sleeping b. being sleeping c. having slept d. having sleeping) when food is unavailable.
3.

_____ (a. To have b. Having had c. Had d. Having) camouflage, or blending in with their
4.

surroundings, is one way that some animals keep from being eaten. Camouflage also allows some

animals _____ (a. to remaining b. to be remaining c. to remain d. remaining) invisible while hunting.
5.

Some animals need _____ (a. to be imitated b. imitating c. having imitated d. to imitate), or mimic,
6.

other animals. These animals have evolved _____ (a. to look b. to have looked c. looking d. having
7.

looked) like other animals to avoid being eaten or to be better hunters. Finally, many animals that

cannot endure _____ (a. live b. living c. to live d. having lived) in the cold escape freezing
8.

temperatures during the winter by _____ (a. to move b. moving c. to be moved d. move) to a
9.

warmer place.

3 | HUMAN DEFENSE

Read this paragraph from a history textbook about how humans defend themselves.
Complete the paragraph. Use the correct forms of the verbs in parentheses.

Equipped with teeth, claws, or other natural weapons, animals have little trouble

_____*finding*_____ food and defending themselves. Humans, on the other hand,
0. (find)

would have a hard time _____ if they did not create special defenses for
1. (survive)

themselves against the weather and other animals. Even _____ clothes is
2. (wear)

a way that we protect ourselves. One way that humans have found to find food to eat and to

protect themselves is by _____ weapons. A weapon can be used
3. (make)

_____ an animal, another person, or to destroy a military target.
4. (injure)

Throughout history, weapons have been used _____ others.
5. (threaten)

_____ weapons was an important step in mankind's progress from
6. (invent)

nomads to farmers. _____ begun to farm the land, people needed
7. (have)

ways to protect their crops and animals from thieves. Also, in the Middle Ages, the

_____ of castles necessitated _____ new
8. (build)   9. (develop)

weapons to help defend the castles. Today there is a constant race _____
10. (improve)

military weapons. This has resulted in the development of the nuclear bomb, which has been

considered too powerful _____ in any modern wars since World War II.
11. (employ)

Countries that possess nuclear weapons are not prepared _____ them
12. (use)

because they do not want to risk _____ themselves as well. The world
13. (hurt)

community closely monitors each country's decision _____ nuclear
14. (produce)

weapons and strongly encourages all countries _____ them. Hopefully,
15. (destroy)

we can avoid _____ them at all in future conflicts.
16. (use)

PART VI

4 | MARTIAL ARTS

Read this response to a question about martial arts on an Internet message board.
Complete the sentences. Use the correct forms of the words in parentheses. (Note: There may be more than one correct answer.)

Q: What is martial arts, and how can I choose the right martial arts school?

A: Martial arts can be described as _____ *a way to defend yourself* _____ without
0. (a way / defend / yourself)

weapons. Types of martial arts include karate, tae-kwon-do, kung fu, and many others. Interest

in martial arts _____ over time. Practicing a martial art can be
1. (seem / increase / steadily)

rewarding. _____ can give a person confidence. No one is
2. (have / learned / a martial art)

_____ from practicing a martial art.
3. (too / old / benefit)

_____ of martial arts to choose will depend on what you
4. (decide / on / which of the many kinds)

prefer to learn. Keep in mind, however, that _____ does not
5. (you / learn / a martial art)

mean that you will use it to fight. Some schools _____ into
6. (try / scare / people)

taking classes _____ that there are dangerous people all
7. (by / convince / them)

around them. However, it would be useless for _____ with a
8. (a person / defend / himself or herself)

martial art against people with guns or knives. Obviously, the best way to defend yourself is to

_____ where you may be in danger. Nevertheless, if you
9. (avoid / spend time / in places)

_____ some new physical skills, a martial arts class can help
10. (feel like / learn)

you do that. I _____ a class or two just to observe.
11. (recommend / attend)

_____, you will not _____ if
12. (without / see / a class)   13. (be able / figure out)

the school is right for you. For instance, some instructors _____
14. (advise / use)

"circular" movements _____, whereas others prefer to teach
15. (attack / or / block)

"linear" styles, using straight movements. Also, _____ may be
16. (earn / different belts)

easy or extremely difficult to do, depending on the school.

5 | EDITING: DEFENDING YOUR HOME AGAINST TERMITES

Read this Internet article about defending your home against termites. There are ten mistakes in the use of gerunds and infinitives. The first mistake is already corrected. Find and correct nine more. (Note 1: There can be more than one way to correct a mistake. Note 2: Count split infinitives as mistakes.)

              to be

Your home is likely ~~being~~ your greatest financial investment. Protect your home from termites is often a great concern. Termites feed on the wood in your home will eventually cause great damage, so you should find a pest control company if you suspect your home has them. It is important making sure that the company is reputable. Take your time to carefully select a good company. You do not need rushing into finding a company since termites work slowly. After you make an appointment, someone will come to thoroughly inspect your home for termites. When the termite inspector arrives, he or she will begin check inside your house as well as outdoors. If termites are found to eating the wood in your house, the inspector will treat the wood to kill the termites. Have been regularly treated for termites, your home will increase in value.

Unit 15 Achievement Test

**30 Items
Score: _____**

🎧 **A.** *Listen to this report about a musician. Complete the report by writing the word(s) that you hear. You will hear the recording two times.*

Daniel Larsen, a writer for musical theater, does not avoid _____*working*_____ hard to reach
0.

his dreams, but then for him, working with music is play. As a youth, Larsen was interested in

_____ a pharmacist like his father. He recalled _____ afraid to
1.   **2.**

pursue his love of music because he was not sure if he would make money. However, he

reconsidered _____ in his father's footsteps after two unhappy years of working as
3.

a pharmacist, and no time for his music. Larsen has always enjoyed _____ music,
4.

so his _____ long hours composing felt more like fun than work. When he finished
5.

_____ his first serious musical, *Soft Step*, he found a local theater and began
6.

_____ it. His big break came when someone from a New York production
7.

company saw the show and proposed _____ it on Broadway. Larsen's following his
8.

dreams was about to pay off, but he had some things to learn before making it big on Broadway.

B. *Read each numbered statement from the report. Then write the letter of the sentence that is closest in meaning to the statement.*

___*c*___ **0.** Daniel Larsen does not avoid working hard to achieve his dreams.
  a. Daniel Larsen does not work hard to achieve his dreams.
  b. Daniel Larsen worked hard so he achieved his dreams.
  c. Daniel Larsen works as hard as he can in order to achieve his dreams.

_____ **1.** Larsen's following his dreams was about to pay off.
  a. Larsen had been following his dreams and as a result, he was becoming successful.
  b. Larsen has to pay off by following his dreams.
  c. Followed by his dreams, Larsen was about to pay off.

_____ **2.** He had some things to learn before making it big on Broadway.
  a. He could make it big on Broadway before learning more things.
  b. He could make it big on Broadway after learning more things.
  c. He was anxious to make it big on Broadway.

2 | IMPROVING THE SHOW

Continue reading about what Larsen had to learn to become successful on Broadway.
*Write **S** if the underlined gerund is used as a subject, **O** if it is used as an object, or **C** if it is*
used as a subject or object complement.

_S_ 0. The first thing Larsen learned was that <u>producing</u> a Broadway show is expensive.

____ 1. The most important thing was <u>figuring</u> out ways to make the show more profitable.

____ 2. He did not have trouble <u>revising</u> parts of the show.

____ 3. <u>Taking</u> suggestions from the musicians was also helpful.

____ 4. He avoided <u>controlling</u> how the songs were sung.

____ 5. One of his main concerns was <u>advertising</u> the show.

3 | OPENING NIGHT

Read more of the report about Larsen. Complete the sentences by writing the gerund form
of each verb.

Before *Soft Step* opened, Larsen went _____*running*_____ to try and relax. All of the
                                          0. (run)

_____ did not lessen his feelings of anxiety. _____ made many
1. (rehearse)   **2. (have)**

improvements to the show, Larsen knew that he had a good musical on his hands, but he was

still nervous about _____ an audience. From the first moment of the show's
                    3. (have)

_____, Larsen kept _____ what the audience was feeling and
4. (open)   **5. (wonder)**

thinking. By the end of the show, Larsen's _____ had reached its peak.
                                            6. (worry)

_____ written the musical himself, he was his own worst critic. The audience,
7. (Have)

however, couldn't resist _____ to their feet and giving the show a 10-minute
                         8. (jump)

standing ovation. As hard as he tried, Larsen could not prevent the tears from

_____ to his eyes. He would never forget the sight of so many people
9. (come)

_____ him and his work.
10. (applaud)

4 | EDITING: THE SHOW'S A HIT!

Read Daniel Larsen's journal. There are six mistakes in the use of gerunds. The first mistake is already corrected. Find and correct five more.

My show has been on Broadway for a month now! I'm thrilled, but I'm so tired that I

feel like ~~to sleep~~ *sleeping* for a week! Have worked so hard for so long, I can't believe I'm finally a

success. I never thought this would happen to me! I enjoy to have the opportunity to work

with such talented people. Fortunately, people are recognizing my name, but not my face, so I

don't need to avoid to be in crowds yet. A Hollywood studio and I are even discussing adapt

the show for the big screen! I really appreciate their help me to follow my dreams.

Unit 16 Achievement Test

🎧 **A.** *Listen to this introduction for a radio science program. Complete the introduction by writing the word(s) that you hear. You will hear the recording two times.*

This is "Science Today," and I'm Michael Edson. There are many ways _____*to say*_____

0.

that something has a smell. We might use the words *fragrance* or *aroma* _____

1.

about a good smell, or if we want _____ that something smells bad, we use *stench*

2.

or *stink*. Dogs and many other animals are lucky (or perhaps not so lucky) _____

3.

a very keen sense of smell. Our noses are not nearly as sensitive, but they are good enough

_____ a leaking gas pipe or food cooking in the kitchen. Our sense of smell also

4.

helps us _____. If you have ever tried _____ a meal when you had a

5.   **6.**

stuffy nose, you will probably remember that the food seemed _____ rather bland,

7.

like it needed _____. This hour on "Science Today," we are going to talk about the

8.

sense of smell. Stay with us.

B. *Read these sentences related to the listening. Write **S** if the infinitive is used as a subject, **O** if it is used as an object, or **C** if it is used as a subject or object complement.*

__*O*__ 0. If we want <u>to say</u> something smells good, we use *fragrance* or *aroma*.

_____ 1. The meal seemed <u>to be flavorless</u> because I had a cold.

_____ 2. The food needs <u>to be cooked</u> longer.

2 | A PLACE TO REMEMBER

Read this Internet article about a study of smell and memory. Choose the best answer to complete the sentences.

A Viking museum in England decided ____*a*____ (**a. to replicate b. replicate c. replicating d. to have**
0.

replicated) more than just the sights and sounds of the life of the Vikings. They also created an

experience _____ (**a. remembering b. remember c. to remember d. to have remembered**) with the help
1.

of smells, including smells of a leather-making shop and the salty ocean. In one study of smell

and memory, 50 participants who had visited the museum were asked _____ (**a. describing**
2.

b. to describe c. describe d. to have described) the museum five years later. Researchers were amazed

_____ (**a. discover b. discovering c. to be discovered d. to discover**) that when the participants were
3.

exposed to identical smells to the ones used in the museum, they were shown _____
4.

(**a. remembering b. to be remembered c. having remembered d. to have remembered**) 20 percent more of

the museum's contents. Since the study was published, many other museums have considered

_____ (**a. to include b. to have included c. including d. having included**) smells in their exhibits.
5.

3 | THE SMELL OF MONEY

Read this newspaper article about a new trend in grocery stores. Complete the sentences.
Use the correct forms of the verbs in parentheses.

More and more grocery stores appear _____ *to be* _____ using aromas
                                          0. (be)

_____ sales. The stores attempt _____ their
        1. (increase)   **2. (lure)**

customers with the smell of fresh bread, fried meat, or chocolate, which tends

_____ customers to certain products they had not intended
        3. (attract)

_____, and makes them more likely _____
        4. (buy)   **5. (spend)**

their money in the store. The aromas can make it difficult for customers

_____ buying whatever they smell. The marketing power of aromas is
        6. (resist)

not _____. Food aromas are believed _____ first
        7. (downplay)   **8. (be)**

used in stores in England, which were said _____ sales by 10 percent.
                                                    9. (increase)

A shopping list and a full stomach may help shoppers to be strong enough

_____ spending money that they did not intend to spend.
        10. (avoid)

4 | EDITING: THE ARTIFICIAL NOSE

Read this magazine article about an artificial nose. There are six mistakes in the use of
infinitives. The first mistake is already corrected. Find and correct five more. (Note 1: There
can be more than one way to correct a mistake. Note 2: Count split infinitives as mistakes.)

                         to develop
Scientists have been working ~~developing~~ an artificial nose. Their nose is designed to

accurately detect toxic chemicals that should not be allowed building up in enclosed spaces.

Many industries have been trying finding a way to quickly identify harmful substances. The

scientists are continuing improve the artificial nose before making it commercially available.

Part VI Achievement Test

1 | LISTENING: FEAR

🎧 **A.** *Listen to this radio advertisement for a program about fear. Complete the advertisement by writing the word(s) that you hear. You will hear the recording two times.*

Today on "The Dan Webb Show," we're talking about fear. Fear is a natural emotion

that most people are able _to keep under control_. It has made it possible for people
0.

_____ themselves from danger since the beginning of time. Some people,
1.

however, do not deal well with negative events, and they seem _____ fear
2.

_____ their lives. You might be surprised _____ about the many
3.   **4.**

faces of fear, so you'll want _____ tuned to the "The Dan Webb Show."
5.

B. *Read these sentences based on the listening passage. Write **S** if the infinitive is used as a subject, **O** if it is used as an object, or **SC** if it is used as a subject complement.*

_O_ 0. Most people are able <u>to keep</u> fear under control.

_____ 1. One of fear's functions is <u>to ensure</u> that people do not live dangerously.

_____ 2. <u>To learn</u> about the many faces of fear might be surprising.

_____ 3. Everyone will want <u>to listen</u> to "The Dan Webb Show" today.

C. *Reread the advertisement. Then read each statement and circle **T** (true) or **F** (false).*

Ⓣ **F** 0. "To keep fear under control is important" means the same as "Keeping fear under control is important."

T **F** 1. "You might be surprised to learn about the many faces of fear" means the same as "You might be surprised learning about the many faces of fear."

T **F** 2. "Some people seem to prefer allowing fear to control their lives" means the same as "Some people seem to prefer to allow fear to control their lives."

2 | HORROR FILMS

Read this paragraph from a book about the history of horror films. Complete the paragraph with the correct verb forms. Write the letter of the best answer on each line.

In the 1950s, some amateur filmmakers found a way ____*a*____ (a. to market b. market
                                                          0.
c. marketing d. to be marketing) themselves: the horror film. _____ (a. Scare b. Having scared c. Scaring
                                                                          1.
d. Being scared) the audience was an easy way to make a buck. Many filmmakers were criticized for

devoting little or no effort to crafting a good story, but their audience didn't seem _____
                                                                                        2.
(a. minding b. having minded c. being minded d. to mind). People were satisfied with _____ (a. having
                                                                                          3.
scared b. being scared c. scaring d. to scare). _____ (a. Used b. Having used c. Being used d. Using)
                                                      4.
imaginative monsters and visual innovations, such as 3-D glasses, allowed filmmakers _____
                                                                                        5.
(a. create b. to create c. creating d. to have created) careers for themselves. In the 1990s, however, with

horror films losing popularity, filmmakers needed _____ (a. looking b. to be looking c. look d. to
                                                    6.
look) for other ways of capturing an audience. They found it necessary _____ (a. to develop
                                                                                    7.
b. develop c. to have developed d. developing) more sophisticated story lines and to have larger budgets

to avoid _____ (a. to lose b. lose c. losing d. having lost) money at the box office. Thanks to better
          8.
story lines and more funds, horror filmmakers today have no trouble _____ (a. to find b. find
                                                                                9.
c. finds d. finding) an audience.

PART VI

3 | CHILDREN AND FEAR

Read this paragraph from an online magazine about children and fear. Complete the
sentences by writing the appropriate form of the verb (gerund or infinitive) on each line.
(Note: There may be more than one correct answer.)

As we mature, we have no trouble _____*understanding*_____ that if someone

0. (understand)

disappears behind a door, they continue to exist. Babies, on the other hand, have a hard time

_____ that something exists if they cannot see it.

1. (believe)

_____ peek-a-boo with a baby is one way to help them learn that

2. (Play)

objects are permanent. Some children also fear discipline. Discipline can be used

_____ raise emotionally stable, happy children. However, inconsistent

3. (help)

discipline has been found _____ confusing to children. Not

4. (be)

_____ discipline and _____ children understand

5. (overdo) **6. (help)**

the reasons behind the discipline by _____ it to them is important. The

7. (explain)

_____ of children requires _____ them

8. (socialize) **9. (teach)**

appropriate ways of expressing strong feelings, including the greatest fear: rejection. It is natural

for young children _____ or bite when they feel rejected or are angry at

10. (hit)

other children. However, when children are playing, parents or caregivers should supervise

closely enough _____ how the children are behaving and be prepared

11. (monitor)

_____ them appropriate social behavior. If parents do not do this, they

12. (teach)

risk their child _____ up to think that such behavior is acceptable. By

13. (grow)

age five, a child's way of _____ with fears may be unique, and their

14. (deal)

strategies for _____ may vary. Although a child's fear may seem

15. (cope)

irrational to some parents, it is probably normal behavior for the child. Therefore, parents may

wish _____ patience when dealing with their child's fears.

16. (practice)

4 | OVERCOMING SHYNESS

Read this introduction to a book about overcoming shyness. Complete the sentences. Use the correct forms of the words in parentheses. (Note: There may be more than one correct answer.)

Are you _____*afraid to talk to strangers*_____? Have you ever been
      0. (afraid / talk / to strangers)

_____ in front of a crowd? _____ is
  1. (nervous / speak)   **2. (overcome / shyness)**

possible. _____ can help, and although it may seem
    3. (learn / certain skills)

challenging at first, these skills are not _____. Understanding
           4. (too / difficult / master)

that everyone wants to be accepted and liked is a good first step. _____
           5. (you / begin / a conversation)

may not make you instantly popular, but if you _____ other
     6. (consistently / focus on / help)

people feel comfortable _____ and smiling at them, you will
    7. (by / talk / to them)

notice that people will be more friendly towards you. _____
        8. (you / make a commitment / overcome)

your fears of rejection will pay off over time. If you _____, it
       9. (dread / be / in social situations)

is probably because of previous negative experiences. The next time you know you're going to be

in a social situation, _____ a list of conversation topics. If you
     10. (try / prepare)

_____, for instance, _____
 11. (dare / go / to a party)   **12. (without / think /ahead of time)**

about what you will say, you may not be _____ to begin a
      13. (able / find / the courage)

conversation. Behavioral psychologists also _____ your
      14. (recommend / be / aware of)

body language. _____ and speaking with volume are
   15. (sit / up / straight)

_____ and should be more inviting than looking at your shoes.
 16. (good skills / practice)

PART VI

5 | EDITING: HALLOWEEN CANDY

Read this Internet article about Halloween candy. There are ten mistakes in the use of gerunds and infinitives. The first mistake is already corrected. Find and correct nine more. (Note 1: There can be more than one way to correct a mistake. Note 2: Count split infinitives as mistakes.)

       Halloween is a holiday celebrated in much of the western world. ~~Dress~~ *Dressing* in costumes and going door to door to ask for candy is a special event for many children. Stores' market of candy has helped shape what Halloween is today, and surely children are happy receive the candy. Some children like to strategically choose a neighborhood where they do not need walking very far between houses. Parents need to thoroughly check all the candy to make sure that it is safe; some might even end up to take a piece of their favorite candy, as it is very tempting! Some parents encourage their children to eat the candy as quickly as possible so that their teeth will not decay from to being in contact with sugar for a long period of time. However, brush teeth immediately after eating candy is probably better for children's dental heath than eat it all at once.

PART VII Diagnostic Test

60 Items
Score: _____

1 | LISTENING: A CURE FOR THE COMMON COLD

🎧 **A.** *Brian and Stephanie are executives at a pharmaceutical company. Listen to their conversation about a cure for the common cold. Complete the conversation by writing the word(s) that you hear. You will hear the recording two times.*

BRIAN: Did you read the paper this morning? There's an article on the front page that says our competitors found a cure for the common cold.

STEPHANIE: I know! The news is _____*everywhere*_____. I heard it on the radio this morning. But I
0.
don't believe it. _____, it can't be true. _____ can there
1. **2.**
be a cure.

BRIAN: What? Why not?

STEPHANIE: Well, _____ we have made some advances in understanding colds, I
3.
don't believe the news _____ cold viruses change all the time.
4.
Plus, there are _____ any facts in the news reports I've heard.
5.
_____, I need to see more proof before I believe it.
6.

BRIAN: Well, _____ the article in black and white. I think you should read it.
7.
Our company may be in trouble.

B. *Read the following phrases adapted from the conversation. Write **D** if the phrase is a dependent clause. Write **I** if the phrase is an independent clause.*

__*I*__ **0.** the news is everywhere

_____ **1.** despite the fact that we have made some advances in understanding colds recently

_____ **2.** since cold viruses change all the time

_____ **3.** I don't believe the news

2 | COLD MYTHS

*Read this magazine article about myths of the common cold. Complete the article with
words and phrases from the box right above the text. Use each word or phrase only once.*

actually	even if	~~perhaps~~
because	home	rather
before	just	upon
despite the fact	only	when
despite the fact that	otherwise	where

_____Perhaps_____ you have heard that becoming cold leads to catching a
0.

cold. _____, this is _____ a myth.
1. **2.**

_____ many people believe it, there is no scientific evidence that it is
3.

true. _____, colds are spread _____ the virus
4. **5.**

enters the body through the nose or eye. _____ a person infected with
6.

the cold can give it to someone else _____ sneezing. The occurrence of
7.

colds may be slightly higher in the winter _____ people are closed
8.

up with other people at _____ or in the office
9.

_____ they are more likely to contract the virus.
10.

actually	because	furthermore	second	third
after	catching	in no way	suffering	to summarize
as soon as	even if	nevertheless		

_____, some people believe that drinking milk while
11.

_____ from a cold worsens congestion. People may think this
12.

_____ the fat in milk is believed to get stuck in the throat.
13.

_____, one study showed that _____ you drink
14. **15.**

a lot of milk, you will not have worse congestion. _____, many people
16.

think that taking medicine may slow recovery from a cold. However, this is

_____ supported by science. _____, treating cold
       17.   **18.**

symptoms may actually help lower the chance of spreading the virus to others.

_____, getting cold does not cause colds, and drinking milk and taking
      19.

medicine are OK after _____ a cold.
                      20.

3 | COLD PREVENTION

Read this Internet article about how to prevent colds. Complete the sentences with the words in parentheses. You may need to change the form of some of the words. Pay attention to the use of punctuation where necessary.

_____*Unfortunately*_____, there is still no cure for the common cold.
    0. (unfortunate)

_____ colds can be prevented, _____
    1. (however)   **2. (provide / you / take)**

some simple precautions. _____, we have come up with some
               3. (after / study / how / colds / spread)

helpful tips to prevent catching or spreading a cold. _____ the
                             4. (obvious)

best way to avoid catching a cold is to avoid contact with others who have a cold.

_____, _____ has
  5. (since / this / is not / always / possible)   **6. (especially / if / someone else / in the home)**

a cold, washing hands often helps. _____ avoid touching your nose and
                      7. (in / addition)

eyes _____ your hands, _____ _____
   8. (before / thoroughly / wash)   **9. (as)**   **10. (even / one / virus)**

can travel from your hand to your nose or eyes and get you sick. If you have a cold yourself, you

_____ about preventing the spread of your cold to others.
   11. (can / never / be / too / cautious)

_____ a cold coming on, you should take medicine.
   12. (as soon as / you / feel)

_____ the cold, it can relieve cold symptoms and protect
   13. (although / the medicine / will not / end)

other people. How? _____ colds can be passed by sneezing, coughing, or
              14. (for example)

touching something _____. _____
          15. (after / blow / your nose)   **16. (give / that / medicine / can / keep)**

you from coughing, sneezing, or having a runny nose, it can lower the chance that you give the

cold to someone else. Besides, you'll feel better. _____, people with colds
                         17. (to / conclude)

_____. There may be a cure for the common cold in the future,
  18. (be everywhere)

_____ _____, we'll just need to be cautious.
  19. (but)   **20. (in / the / meantime)**

PART VII

4 | EDITING: UNANSWERED QUESTIONS

Read this paragraph from a science journal article about the unanswered questions about colds. There are ten mistakes in the paragraph. Find and correct ten more. The first mistake is already corrected. (Note: There may be more than one way to correct a mistake.)

                                                                          For example

There are still many unanswered questions regarding the cold virus. ~~For an example~~, where do they come from? Even if virologists, people who study viruses, have a poor understanding of their origin. Changed over time, cold viruses are easily not studied. Giving that viruses have ever been observed while changed, scientists barely understand the process. Because these reasons, it is difficult to find a cure, but many scientists are hopeful that a cure is still possible. Said one scientist, "As long that we continue to study colds, we will learn new things. Nor we should never give up trying to find a cure. Unless, we never will."

Unit 17 Achievement Test

30 Items
Score: _____

1 | LISTENING: WHAT DOES THE EXPERT SAY? PART I

🎧 ***A.*** *Listen to Part 1 of a radio interview with a family therapist, Dr. Krishna Das. Complete the interview by writing the word(s) that you hear. You will hear the recording two times.*

WORLD REVIEW: Dr. Das, you mention in your book that television is one factor contributing to

the breakdown of the family. Please talk about that.

DAS: Certainly. Today, we _____*often*_____ find that both parents have to work

0.

to make ends meet. _____ do they have enough time for all

1.

the things they want and need to do. When these parents come

_____ from work _____, they are usually

2.   3.

_____ tired. Unfortunately, they will use the television as a

4.

babysitter, just so they can get some chores done. However, if a television is on

constantly, as it is in many homes, there are certainly fewer opportunities for

the members of the family to interact and to communicate.

B. *Read the underlined adverbs in these sentences adapted from the reading. Write **S** if the adverb is a sentence adverb, **F** if it is a focus adverb, and **Fre** if it is an adverb of frequency.*

_*S*_ 0. Today, we <u>often</u> find that both parents have to work to make ends meet.

_____ 1. When working parents come home, they are <u>usually</u> tired.

_____ 2. <u>Unfortunately</u>, they will use the television as a babysitter.

_____ 3. Many parents turn on the television <u>just</u> so they can get some chores done.

_____ 4. If a television is on <u>constantly</u>, there are fewer opportunities to interact.

_____ 5. If a television is on constantly, there are <u>certainly</u> fewer opportunities for the members of

the family to interact and to communicate.

PART VII

2 | SHOULD PARENTS WORK LESS?

*Read more of the interview with Dr. Das. Find and underline 10 sentence, focus, or negative adverbs in the manuscript. Above each adverb, write **S** if it is a sentence adverb, **F** if it is a focus adverb, or **N** if it is a negative adverb. An example is given.*

                                  S

WORLD REVIEW: <u>Obviously</u>, parents should spend more time with their children, but this isn't

easy to do, is it?

DAS: No, it isn't. Because parents work a lot, rarely do they have the energy to play

with their children or to read to them. Parents just need to be able to say to

their children, "Tonight, we're not watching any TV."

WR: You mention that parents are simply too tired to spend time with their children

after work. Should parents work fewer hours?

DAS: Certainly, parents need to work to be able to provide for their families, but

obviously, parents need to spend time with their children as well, and not just

provide food, clothing, and shelter. If parents can manage to work only part

time, not only will they be less stressed, but their children will clearly benefit as

well. But, in many cases, working part time isn't even an option for parents.

3 | MORE EXPERT ADVICE

*Read more sentences adapted from the interview with Dr. Das. Fill in each blank with an
appropriate word from the box. There may be more than one answer for some items.*

almost	even	neither	rarely	seldom
basically	just	~~only~~	sadly	simply
certainly				

0. But that's _____ *only* _____ the beginning.

1. You can watch _____ one hour of TV tonight.

2. But far more important is their need _____ to be with their children.

3. Parents need to work _____ in many well-off families.

4. _____, many parents find it difficult to get involved with their children.

5. _____ do they have enough time for all the things they want to do.

6. _____ do they have enough energy to play with their children.

7. Yes, it's _____ a difficult issue.

4 | EDITING: PARENTS' REACTION TO THE EXPERT

*Read this conversation between a husband and wife who just listened to the radio
interview with Dr. Das. There are five mistakes in the use of adverbs. The first mistake is
already corrected. Find and correct four more. (Note: There can be more than one way to
correct a mistake.)*

SPIRO: *World Review* ~~has usually~~ ^{usually has} great guests, but I don't know about today's guest.

ROULA: Well, I think Dr. Das is right—rarely we get a chance to spend enough time with our

kids. But no way we can work part time! Never I have heard such an unrealistic idea!

SPIRO: There someone is out of touch with reality!

Unit 18 Achievement Test

30 Items
Score: _____

1 | LISTENING: WHAT DOES THE EXPERT SAY? PART II

○ **A.** *Listen to Part II of an interview with family therapist Dr. Krishna Das. Complete the interview by writing the word(s) that you hear. You will hear the recording two times.*

WORLD REVIEW: Dr. Das, _____*when*_____ you were here last time, we talked about
0.

how television can influence a family. Today, let's turn our attention to

communication. Communication seems to be deteriorating _____
1.

we look. Why is that?

DAS: Time is one factor. _____ people are so busy, they are less likely
2.

to communicate face to face.

WR: What about the role of television?

DAS: Television may also reduce communication between family members

_____ it is often difficult to watch TV and carry on a
3.

conversation at the same time. _____ television was widespread,
4.

there were more quality conversations. TV may especially influence children's

development of communication skills _____ they don't have as
5.

much interaction with others _____ children did before
6.

television. _____ children watch only one hour of TV per day,
7.

they tend to have worse communication skills than children who watch no TV.

B. *Read the last paragraph in the interview with Dr. Das. Underline the independent clauses. There are four of them.*

C. *Read these sentences adapted from the interview in Part A. Write* **C** *if the underlined word is an adverb of condition,* **P** *if it is an adverb of place, or* **R** *if it is an adverb of reason.*

___R___ **0.** Television may also restrict communication <u>because</u> it is difficult to watch TV and carry on a conversation at the same time.

_____ **1.** Quality conversations seem to be decreasing <u>everywhere</u> we look.

_____ **2.** TV may especially influence children's development of communication skills <u>because</u> they don't have as much interaction with others as children did before television.

_____ **3.** Children are more likely to develop better communication skills <u>if</u> they don't watch TV.

_____ **4.** You can't have a conversation in movie theaters <u>unless</u> you are the only ones in the theater.

2 | IMPROVING A COMPANY

A panel of experts has been investigating how to improve a large company. Write their conclusions by combining each of the following pairs of sentences into one sentence with a dependent clause and an independent clause. Place the idea that seems more important in the independent clause. Use the indicated subordinating conjunctions. Do not add words. There might be more than one way to combine sentences.

0. They can resell them. Some clients buy our products. (so that)

   Some clients buy our products so that they can resell them.
_____

1. Profitability will be high. Demand is high. (as long as)

_____

2. Many people support less packaging. Excess packaging is seen as wasteful. (because)

_____

_____

3. Others support less packaging. They recognize that the packaging helps protect the product. (although)

_____

_____

4. Teenagers are targeted by marketing specifically. They are not likely to buy our products. (unless)

_____

_____

5. Gas is more expensive. The price of the products needs to be increased to pay for distribution. (now that)

_____

_____

6. Second purchases have increased. The number of first-time buyers has decreased. (whereas)

_____

_____

7. Customers buy our products three times or more. They will be sent a "frequent buyer" promotional advertisement. (if)

_____

_____

8. The latest product is not that popular. Some people love it. (even though)

_____

9. Research and development continues to try to improve the products. The recognition of the products should remain constant. (while)

_____

_____

10. Most of the company's advertising is done on television. There is much evidence that radio advertising could be cost effective. (despite the fact that)

_____

_____

3 | EDITING: WHERE SHOULD WE OPEN OUR BUSINESS?

Bradley and Jennifer plan to open a new clothing store for children. Read their conversation about where they should open their business. There are six mistakes in the use of conjunctions. The first mistake is already corrected. Find and correct five more. (Note: There can be more than one way to correct a mistake.)

BRADLEY: Jennifer, I've got two possible locations for our new business. One is nearby, not too far from a school, and it is located on a quiet road. The other is in the mall downtown. Which one do you think we should take?

JENNIFER: Well, ~~although~~ *if* we take the location that is nearby, we won't have to spend a lot of time driving to work. Driving to the mall daily would take about an hour of our time whereas it is about 15 miles away on a busy road.

BRADLEY: True, but we would probably have more customers at the mall. You know, so many people go to the mall for different reasons. Although they see our store, they might just stop in.

JENNIFER: That's possible, but remember, we are selling children's clothes. While we let parents know about our business, I think a school location might work out great!

BRADLEY: Well, since we decide for sure, let's visit both locations. After it will take some time, I think seeing both places will help us in our decision.

Unit 19 Achievement Test

1 | LISTENING: POPULATION GROWTH

🎧 *Listen to the introduction to the talk radio program, "World View." Complete the introduction by writing the word(s) that you hear. You will hear the recording two times.*

Welcome to "World View." I'm Desiree Savage. There are more people on the Earth today

than ever before. This means there is also more food available, _____*allowing*_____ people to

0.

survive on the one hand, but _____ more of the world's resources on the other.

1.

_____ the world's population continues to rise, some scientists believe that slowing

2.

population growth is necessary.

2 | POPULATION GROWTH IN CHINA

🎧 *Listen to and read the next part of the talk radio program. Then complete the exercises below. You will hear the recording two times.*

Observing that population is growing faster than our ability to produce food, some scientists believe that it is desirable to stop population growth. How would this work? Having reached childbearing age, parents would have only two children. Economists, on the other hand, argue that it is not possible for a country to have economic growth while limiting population growth. China has been the country most concerned with slowing its population growth. While discussing the problem, Chinese government officials realized that China would not be able to support the population growth much longer. Before limiting the size of Chinese families, the members of the Chinese government consulted with scientists to see what the effects would be. After realizing that the benefits would outweigh the disadvantages, the Chinese government adopted a policy of allowing only one child per family. We'll be talking about the effects of China's population policy today on "World View."

A. *In the paragraph above, find four adverb phrases with a subordinating conjunction and write them below.*

0. *while limiting population growth* _____

1. _____

2. _____

3. _____

B. In the paragraph in Exercise 2, find two adverbial phrases without a subordinating conjunction and write them below.

1. _____

2. _____

| 3 | NEWS SHORTS |

Read these news shorts from an Internet news website. Then read the following sentences and decide whether the second sentence has the same basic meaning as the first. Write **Yes** *or* **No**.

The cease-fire has been broken in Franconia. Asked whether he would attend the peace conference in Geneva, Hernando Amalde declined to commit himself, saying that the success of the conference depends on Mr. Tintor, the country's president. Interviewed about Mr. Amalde's comments, an aide to President Tintor, speaking on condition of anonymity, said he expected the peace conference to take place as planned. Losing support for the war, President Tintor is expected to announce plans for a peace treaty while attending the conference.

After receiving additional funding, scientists at the World Space Association announced plans to build a new space telescope. Having made improvements in technology, the scientists promised that the new telescope would be four times more powerful than any existing space telescope. Government officials, while meeting with the organization's president, agreed to provide the necessary billion dollars after learning that popular support for space exploration is at an all-time high.

0. Asked whether he would attend the peace conference in Geneva, Amalde declined to commit

   himself.

   Yes When asked whether he would attend the peace conference in Geneva, Amalde declined

   to commit himself.

1. Amalde declined to commit himself, saying that the success of the conference depends on Mr.

   Tintor, the country's president.

   _____ Amalde declined to commit himself, having said that the success of the conference

   depends on Mr. Tintor, the country's president.

2. Interviewed about Mr. Amalde's comments, an aide to President Tintor said he expected the

   peace conference to take place as planned.

   _____ When he was interviewed about Mr. Amalde's comments, an aide to President Tintor

   said he expected the peace conference to take place as planned.

3. An aide to President Tintor, speaking on condition of anonymity, said he expected the peace conference to take place as planned.

   _____ An aide to President Tintor told the reporter that he expected the peace conference to take place as planned, but he did not want the reporter to mention his name.

4. Losing support for the war, President Tintor is expected to announce plans for a peace treaty at the conference.

   _____ Having lost support for the war, President Tintor is expected to announce plans for a peace treaty at the conference.

5. President Tintor is expected to announce plans for a peace treaty while attending the conference.

   _____ President Tintor is expected to announce plans for a peace treaty while he attends the conference.

6. After receiving additional funding, scientists at the World Space Association announced plans to build a new space telescope.

   _____ Receiving additional funding, scientists at the World Space Association announced plans to build a new space telescope.

7. Having made improvements in technology, the scientists promised that the new telescope would be four times more powerful than any existing space telescope.

   _____ Making improvements in technology, the scientists promised that the new telescope would be four times more powerful than any existing space telescope.

8. Government officials, while meeting with the organization's president, agreed to provide the necessary billion dollars.

   _____ Government officials met with the organization's president and agreed to provide the necessary billion dollars.

9. Government officials agreed to provide the necessary billion dollars after learning that popular support for space exploration is at an all-time high.

   _____ Government officials agreed to provide the necessary billion dollars after they learned that popular support for space exploration is at an all-time high.

4 | WORLD ISSUES

Combine each of the following pairs of sentences into one sentence. Use the prompts in parentheses. There might be more than one way to combine sentences.

0. World leaders feel safer. World leaders agreed to outlaw chemical weapons. (*since*)

World leaders feel safer since agreeing to outlaw chemical weapons.

1. Some people want to limit the size of their family. They are concerned with overpopulation. (adverbial phrase)

_____

_____

2. The world's population grew slowly between the years 500 and 1700. It then began to accelerate. (*having* + past participle)

_____

_____

3. More and more land is cleared for farms every year. This destroys animal habitats. (present participle)

_____

_____

4. World leaders attended the conference on nuclear waste. They agreed to invest money into disposing the waste safely. (*while* + present participle)

_____

_____

5. United Nations arms inspectors visited the military base. They reported their findings to the council. (*after* + present participle)

_____

_____

PART VII

6. Many parents want more than two children. They oppose zero population growth. (present participle)

_____

7. The president first met with his task force. He hosted a conference on environmental concerns. (*before* + present participle)

_____

_____

5 | EDITING: SUMMARY

Read this paragraph from a magazine article. There are seven mistakes in the use of adverb and adverbial phrases. The first mistake is already corrected. Find and correct six more. (Note: There can be more than one way to correct a mistake.)

Observing

~~To observe~~ that population and food supply grow at different rates, Malthus warned us of a problem. Wrote in an essay, Malthus claimed that the world's population would grow faster than our ability to produce food. If carrying out correctly, the adoption of zero population growth would cause the population to stabilize. Before pass a law to limit population growth, Chinese government officials discussed the advantages and disadvantages with many experts. Established a policy of limiting births, Chinese government officials had to enforce it. Although they have largely been successful, since having adopted the policy, China's population growth slowing, but nevertheless continues to rise.

Unit 20 Achievement Test

30 Items
Score: _____

---

1 | LISTENING: METRO

🎧 **A.** *Listen to this local radio commentary about building a metro. Complete the radio commentary by writing the word(s) that you hear. You will hear the recording two times.*

_____*When*_____ the car was invented, I don't think anyone could
0.

have predicted how it would change the world. It is convenient to travel by car.

_____, there are disadvantages to having so many cars.
1.

_____, cars are so widespread today that traffic is terrible in many cities,
2.

including our own. For this reason, I propose that we build an underground metro. The metro

should be attractive _____ convenient; otherwise, people will not use it.
3.

In Paris, _____, you can buy a metro pass that will take you anywhere
4.

the metro goes. _____, it takes time to build an underground metro.
5.

Meanwhile, people should depend on buses. _____, we need to do
6.

something about the terrible traffic in our city, and I think a metro would help solve the problem.

B. *Read the sentences from the local radio commentary. Write the letter of the answer that is closest to the meaning of the original sentence.*

___*b*___ 0. When the car was invented, I don't think anyone could have predicted how it would change the world.
    a. Since the car was invented, I don't think anyone could have predicted how it would change the world.
    b. At the time the car was invented, I don't think anyone could have predicted how it would change the world.
    c. In such an event that the car was invented, I don't think anyone could have predicted how it would change the world.
    d. As a result of the invention of the car, I don't think anyone could have predicted how it would change the world.

_____ 1. For this reason, I propose that we build an underground metro.
    a. Because of this, I propose that we build an underground metro.
    b. During this time, I propose that we build an underground metro.
    c. At any rate, I propose that we build an underground metro.
    d. In the same way, I propose that we build an underground metro.

PART VII

_____ 2. Otherwise, people will not use it.
     a. Nevertheless, people will not use it.
     b. Most importantly, people will not use it.
     c. As a matter of fact, people will not use it.
     d. If not, people will not use it.

_____ 3. Meanwhile, people should depend on buses.
     a. However, people should depend on buses.
     b. In spite of this, people should depend on buses.
     c. At the same time, people should depend on buses.
     d. In either case, people should depend on buses.

2 | TRAFFIC AND STRESS

Read this paragraph from the Internet about simplifying your life. Complete the text with connectors from the box. Use each connector only once.

along with	before	for instance	~~indeed~~
and	first	however	otherwise
as a result			

_____Indeed_____, cars have certainly made travel easier. _____, cars
    0.   **1.**

have their down side as well. _____ better mobility comes more stress.
                                 2.

_____ of all, the car is available to nearly everyone, _____ huge
    3.   **4.**

traffic jams are created _____. Second, cars and car insurance provide a financial
                            5.

stress on many families. _____, the average person with a new car needs to work
                            6.

for an entire year just to pay for the car. Clearly, we need to think about how necessary it is to

own a car; _____ we might have more stress in our lives than we want or need.
        7.

3 | DRIVING TEST

Alice Wu is a driver's license test examiner. Read her statements to people about how they did on their tests. Use the connector in parentheses to either combine the following pairs of sentences or to create two new sentences. Pay attention to the use of punctuation.

0. Mr. Matos, you passed the exam / you have expert road knowledge. (because)

   Mr. Matos, you passed the exam because you have expert road knowledge.

1. Mr. Matos, you passed the exam because of your expert road knowledge / you could use some practice in parallel parking. (however)

   _____

   _____

2. Bob, when you parked uphill, you didn't turn your wheels away from the curb / you would have passed. (otherwise)

   _____

   _____

3. Jan, you didn't use a signal when you turned left at the intersection / you didn't signal when you turned into the parking lot. (likewise)

   _____

   _____

4. Mrs. Thomas, you lost some points / you scraped the curb when you parked. (on account of this)

   _____

   _____

5. Bernie, you didn't notice the car behind you trying to pass you / you were changing lanes. (meanwhile)

   _____

   _____

PART VII

6. Alison, when the ambulance was approaching, first you should have signaled to pull over / you should have slowed down. (then)

_____

_____

7. Ms. Adams, on the last part of the test you parked perfectly / you did very well. (all in all)

_____

_____

8. Alex, you lost some points by stopping too close behind the other car / you did everything else correctly. (though)

_____

_____

9. Stephanie, signaling before you change lanes is very important / especially / a car is behind you. (when)

_____

_____

| 4 | EDITING: NEIGHBORS ON THE GO |

Read this commentary from a magazine. There are six mistakes in the use of connectors.
The first mistake is already corrected. Find and correct five more. (Note: There can be more
than one way to correct a mistake.)

~~After~~ everyone had cars, people knew their neighbors so they would walk past each other
Before
when they came or went. Today, most people are isolated in their own cars. On the contrary,
we have less social interaction with our neighbors. Most important, we have become less
understanding of one another. Meanwhile, cars have weakened our neighborhoods. In
addition, I would like to invite you to go for a walk around your neighborhood once in a
while, and if you see a neighbor, stop and introduce yourself.

Part VII Achievement Test

---

1 | LISTENING: INVITATION TO A FAMILY REUNION

🎧 **A.** *Brad and Linda just received an invitation to a family reunion. Listen to their conversation. Complete the conversation by writing the word(s) that you hear. You will hear the recording two times.*

BRAD: Did you see the letter from Aunt Helen? She's hosting a family reunion.

LINDA: I know! I saw it ___*as soon as*___ I got home. But I was thinking that
                    0.

_____ it's a mistake. _____ did I ever think I would hear
      1.   **2.**

from her.

BRAD: What? Why not?

LINDA: Well, _____ I have no problem with her, she and Mom stopped talking
          3.

years ago _____ Helen got all Grandpa's land when he died.
                 4.

_____, I've _____ even met her.
     5.   **6.**

BRAD: Well, _____ her number in the letter. Let's call her and find out more
          7.

about the reunion.

B. *Read the following phrases adapted from the conversation. Write* **D** *if the phrase is a dependent clause. Write* **I** *if the phrase is an independent clause.*

___*I*___ **0.** I saw it as soon as I got home

_____ **1.** although I have no problem with her

_____ **2.** due to the fact that Helen got all Grandpa's land when he died

_____ **3.** her number is in the letter

2 | FAMILY REUNIONS: THE BEST TIMES OF MY LIFE

Alana, a student, has written an essay about the best times of her life. Complete the essay with words and phrases from the box right above the text.

although	fortunately	~~maybe~~	then
as a matter of fact	in addition	only	when

_____ Maybe _____ you have heard stories about family reunion nightmares.
       0.

_____ for me, these have _____ been stories.
    1.   **2.**

_____ I'm sure some family reunions are disasters, mine have always
    3.

been terrific. _____, some of my favorite memories are from
             4.

_____ I was at family reunions during the summer.
    5.

although	next	since	wherever
besides	only	upon	work

    First of all, it's nice just to talk with family members you don't see very often.

_____ arriving at _____ we're meeting,
    6.   **7.**

I'm always thrilled to see everyone again, and it's a good reminder that I'm not the

_____ one growing older! Some years, some people can't come
    8.

_____ they need to be at _____, but when
    9.   **10.**

they come the next year, we have even more to talk about.

as	however	likewise	playing
even if	in summary	otherwise	second

_____, we all have fun while _____ games
    11.   **12.**

together. I actually don't really care for games _____ I usually lose.
             13.

_____, _____ I don't win, it's nice just being
    14.   **15.**

with family.

| although | as if | in no way | third |
| anyway | coming | incidentally | to this end |

_____, the food is always wonderful! I am
        16.

_____ a cook, so I eat better at my family reunions than at any other
    17.

time of the year. _____, I usually put on a few pounds that I have to lose
        18.

after _____ home! _____, I'm glad our family
     19.   **20.**

has family reunions.

3 | PLANNING A FAMILY REUNION

*Read this Internet article with tips on planning a family reunion. Complete the sentences
with the words in parentheses. You may need to change the form of some of the words. Pay
attention to the use of punctuation where necessary.*

You're planning a family reunion, _____*but fortunately*_____, you don't have to
        0. (but / fortunate)

do it alone. _____ hundreds of successful family reunions, we
    1. (after / study)

have compiled some helpful tips on planning yours. Tip #1, decide who your family is.

_____, choosing who to invite can
    2. (interesting)

_____. Does "family" include only direct descendents of
    3. (actual / be / quite / difficult)

Grandpa George, or cousins, in-laws, and so on? Tip #2, organize a committee.

_____ can be incredibly time-consuming,
    4. (because / plan / a reunion)

_____ can be invaluable.
    5. (have / even / a little / help)

_____, you can communicate
    6. (even if / you / are not / close)

_____. _____, figure out
    7. (by / phone/ or / by / e-mail)   **8. (additional)**

which responsibilities need to be fulfilled _____,
        9. (before / request / help)

_____ to know what their role should be in helping you.
    10. (because / your assistants / will / want)

Tip #3, overprepare. You _____.
        11. (can / never / be / too / prepared)

_____, they will need food, a place to sleep, and
    12. (as soon as / family / arrive)

entertainment. Don't rely on others to provide them with these things.

_____, _____ your cousin
    13. (for / example)   **14. (even / if / you / have asked)**

Joe to bring hot dogs, you may find _____ that he has

15. (after / light / the barbecue)

forgotten them. _____, especially when it comes to money or

16. (give / that / people / can be / unpredictable)

food, tell your family how you expect them to contribute, but plan as though they won't

contribute anything. _____,

17. (to / conclude)

_____ can have a great time at family reunions,

18. (families / everywhere)

_____. _____, only the good

19. (but / there / can be/ a lot of work)   **20. (afterwards / however)**

memories usually remain.

---

4 | EDITING: REUNION ACTIVITIES

*Read this paragraph from the Internet about family reunion activities. There are 11
mistakes in the paragraph. Find and correct 10 more.*

     There are many activities you can do to help make your family reunion a success.

    For instance

~~From instance~~, you can tell stories, have a family talent show, talk about family history, or

even if make a time capsule. Such activities are neither only fun, but they encourage everyone

to interact closely, and to get to know each other better. In result, everyone will feel more

comfortable, especially if they haven't seen each other for a long time. Varied the type of

activities, from sports to crafts to guessing games, you'll ensure that everyone can get

involving. Being giving everyone a choice of activities to do at any one time can also help.

While being planning the activities, it is a good idea to send a questionnaire to everyone you

are inviting to see what they are interested in doing. Be sure to include a self-addressed,

stamped envelope. Unless, you may not get as many responses that you would like. For more

family reunion activity ideas, <u>click to here</u>.

PART VIII Diagnostic Test

1 | LISTENING: PRIVATE VERSUS PUBLIC SCHOOLS

🎧 **A.** *Listen to this news report about private and public high schools. Complete the news report by writing the word(s) that you hear. You will hear the recording two times.*

Where parents send their children to school is an important decision, and experts
0.

_____ all the advantages and disadvantages of both public
1.

and private schools before making a decision. However, some people don't know

_____ different. This report may help.
2.

In the United States, the issue of _____ is what differentiates
3.

public and private schools. While the government pays for public schools, organizations not

associated with the government pay for private schools. Private schools also charge students

tuition, which is a fee that helps pay for the costs of instruction. One disadvantage of private

schools is _____. The fact that private schools charge tuition is one
4.

reason many children go to public schools. Since private schools are not paid for by the

government, they do not have to follow certain government regulations. For example, last year

many parents _____ their children to private schools for religious
5.

training. (The U.S. government _____ in public schools.)
6.

Additionally, in public schools the government decides what requirements to follow for

attendance and graduation, while private schools may establish some of their own requirements.

_____ this freedom can vary considerably. Most private schools
7.

_____ the needs of their students before they decide school policies.
8.

Whether to send your child to a private or public school is a big decision. Parents must

recognize that each type of school is very different. Experts _____
9.

carefully research any school they are considering to see _____ right
10.

for their children.

B. Reread the news report. Find two noun clauses used as subjects and two used as objects. Write them in the table below. (Note: Use only clauses that are given in the news report. Do not use any clauses that you wrote).

NOUN CLAUSE AS A SUBJECT	NOUN CLAUSE AS AN OBJECT
The fact that private schools charge tuition	what requirements to follow for attendance and graduation
1. _____	1. _____
2. _____	2. _____

---

2 | READING: CHALLENGING STUDENTS TO LEARN

Read this conversation about how schools can challenge students more. Then read the statements that change parts of the conversation to indirect speech below. Is the suggested change to indirect speech correct (**C**) or incorrect (**I**)? Circle the correct answer.

BOB: The educational system should challenge students to learn more. Schools can set much higher standards that will motivate students.

YIYUN: I agree. Schools should require more math and science classes. I believe more math and science instruction will help students achieve success in other areas of their lives.

ANA: Bob, do you agree that math and science are what we should teach more?

BOB: No, I don't. I think more language, music, and art classes are necessary.

YIYUN: Here's something we haven't thought about. Where are the schools going to get the money to make these changes?

ANA: You're right, Yiyun. This question is very important.

C ⓘ 0. Bob claimed schools can set higher standards that will motivate students.

C I 1. Yiyun said schools should require students to take more math and science classes.

C I 2. Yiyun said that she believed more math and science instruction will help students achieve success.

C I 3. Ana asked Bob whether or not he agreed that math and science is what we should teach more.

C I 4. Bob told he did not agree.

C I 5. Bob thought that more language, music, and art classes were necessary.

C I   6. Yiyun asked where are the schools going to get funding to make those changes.

C I   7. Ana told Yiyun she was right.

C I   8. Ana told that this question was very important.

3 | TALKING ABOUT SCHOOLS

Read this conversation between Amy, a high school student, and Derek, a college student. Then complete Derek's account of the conversation with indirect speech forms. (Note: Some items may have more than one possible answer.)

    AMY: Did you go to a public or a private high school?

DEREK: I went to a public school.

    AMY: What do you think about public schools in general?

DEREK: The student diversity is always great. In most public schools, students come from all over. When I was in high school, I enjoyed meeting new people all the time in my classes and in different activities.

    AMY: Really? I can't imagine what that would be like!

DEREK: Why? Do you go to a private school?

    AMY: Yes, I do. I like my school because of how small it is. I know all the other students and the teachers. It doesn't matter how shy I am.

DEREK: How many students are in your grade?

    AMY: There are about 40.

DEREK: Wow, that's very small! Do you *really* like going to school there?

    AMY: Yes, I love it! What's better than spending the day with people you know well?

Amy is now in college, and Derek summarizes their conversation to another friend.

DEREK: My friend Amy asked me <u>if I had gone to a public or a private</u> high school. I told her
                                                    0.

_____ to a public school. Amy asked me
                       1.

_____ about public schools in general, and I told her
                       2.

_____ great. I told her that in most public schools,
                       3.

_____ from all over. I told her
                       4.

_____ meeting new people. Amy said that she couldn't
                       5.

imagine _____. I asked her
                       6.

_____ to a private school. She told me
                       7.

_____. She said _____ her
             8.   **9.**

school because of _____. She mentioned that she knew all
                       10.

the other students and teachers. She said it didn't matter

_____. I asked her _____ in her

  11.   12.

grade. She said _____ about 40. I thought that was very

                              13.

small, and I asked her _____ going to school there. Amy

                                            14.

said _____. She asked me _____

                  15.   16.

than spending the day with people you knew well.

---

4 | APPLYING TO A PRIVATE SCHOOL

Mrs. Ryan is considering sending her son to Winslow Academy, a private school. Read this conversation between Mrs. Ryan and Mr. Short, the principal of Winslow Academy. Then complete the statements in indirect speech below. (Note: Some items may have more than one possible answer.)

MRS. RYAN: Why should my son go to school at Winslow Academy?

MR. SHORT: Winslow Academy is the best private school in the city at this time.

MRS. RYAN: What are some advantages of the school?

MR. SHORT: What people always say is the best thing about the school is its small class sizes.

MRS. RYAN: How can Winslow Academy's small classes make my son's education better?

MR. SHORT: Smaller classes allow more teacher-student contact here.

MRS. RYAN: How are students chosen to attend Winslow Academy each year?

MR. SHORT: We always have a very selective admission policy.

MRS. RYAN: What do you mean by "selective admission policy"?

MR. SHORT: It allows us to accept only the brightest and most talented students every year.

MRS. RYAN: Did Winslow Academy accept most students who applied last year?

MR. SHORT: No, not at all. How many students we accept each year depends on the number of qualified applicants.

MRS. RYAN: Well, can you interview my son? He's a very smart and motivated student.

MR. SHORT: I'd like very much to meet your son. When can he come in for an interview?

0. Mrs. Ryan asked _____*why her son should go to school*_____ at Winslow Academy.

1. Mr. Short said _____ in the city at that time.

2. Mrs. Ryan asked _____.

3. Mr. Short said that _____ the school is its small class sizes.

4. Mrs. Ryan asked _____ her son's education better.

5. Mr. Short said _____ more teacher-student contact there.

6. Mrs. Ryan asked _____ to attend Winslow Academy each

   year.

7. Mr. Short said _____ a very selective admission policy.

8. Mrs. Ryan asked _____ by "selective admission policy."

9. Mr. Short told _____ them to accept only the brightest and most talented students.

10. Mrs. Ryan asked _____ most students the previous year.

11. Mr. Short said _____ each year depends on the number of qualified applicants.

12. Mrs. Ryan asked _____ her son.

13. Mr. Short asked _____ for an interview.

---

5 | EDITING: A LETTER HOME

Mariela has just moved into the dorms at a private school. Read this letter that Mariela wrote to her parents. There are 12 mistakes in the use of noun clauses. Find and correct 11 more. (Note: There can be more than one way to correct a mistake.)

Dear Mom and Dad,

    I just wanted to tell ^you that my new school is great! I didn't know how much would it challenge me to do my best. My math teacher asked me do I want to participate in a math competition next month. Of course I said her that I did! It will be a lot of fun is obvious. I need to get ready for the competition, but I don't know what should I study. My new friend Sarah is going too, so I asked her did she know how to prepare. She told that she didn't know either, so we are going to ask the teacher what do we need to know.

    One thing I don't like about the new school is that do I have to wear a uniform. What we wear are very stylish, but I tell that it is boring to wear the same thing every day. Oh well, I'm sure I'll get used to it. I'm off to go study.

Love,

Mariela

Unit 21 Achievement Test

1 | LISTENING: WHO *REALLY* INVENTED THE COMPUTER?

○ *A. Listen to this narrative about the first electronic digital computer. Complete the narrative by writing the word(s) that you hear. You will hear the recording two times.*

Many people think *the first electronic digital computer* was invented in Pennsylvania by

                             0.

John Mauchly and J. Presper Eckert. In fact, records say _____ for

                                                       1.

a patent for their computer in 1946. However, in 1973 a court decided that two other men, John

Vincent Atanasoff and Clifford Berry, were the legal inventors of the first electronic digital

computer. How could this have happened? Who were the real inventors?

It was well known _____ by Atanasoff and one of his graduate

                                          2.

students, Clifford Berry, from 1937 to 1942. They built their computer in the basement of the

physics building at Iowa State University in Ames, Iowa. _____ was

                                                       3.

its use of binary arithmetic, which is a way of representing numbers with only ones and zeros.

The 700-pound machine used this system to perform 150 billion operations in 15 seconds.

John Mauchly, an engineer from Philadelphia who had corresponded with Atanasoff about

his work, visited Atanasoff in 1940 while Atanasoff was building his computer. It isn't known

_____ or what Atanasoff showed Mauchly, but several years later

                                   4.

Mauchly had built his own electronic digital computer in Pennsylvania!

Eventually, a court battle took place about who should collect profits from Mauchly and

Eckert's computer. One organization did not want to pay Mauchly and Eckert because they knew

_____ had been developed earlier by Atanasoff and Berry. So how

                                   5.

did the confusion happen? What many claim is that Atanasoff began the patent process for his

invention, but he had to leave the university suddenly in 1942 for government work concerning

World War II. Why the university failed to complete the patent during his absence remains a

mystery. While some people may not have realized the importance of Atanasoff's invention at the

time, historians now state _____ electronic digital computer ever

                                          6.

developed. Unfortunately, professors in the physics department at Iowa State University claim

_____ because storage space was needed in the basement. However,
      7.

a model of the original computer was completed at Iowa State University in 1997 to honor

Atanasoff and Berry and their significant invention.

B. *Reread the narrative. Then read each statement and circle* **T** *(true) or* **F** *(false).*

T   F   0. In 1973, a court decided that Mauchly and Eckert were the legal inventors of
the computer.

T   F   1. No one knows what Atanasoff showed Mauchly.

T   F   2. Many people know why the university didn't file the patent application.

T   F   3. Many people claim Atanasoff began to file a patent for his invention but had to
leave.

C. *Reread the narrative. Find one example of a noun clause used as a subject and one
example of a noun clause used as an object. (Note: Use only clauses that are given in the
narrative. Do not use any clauses that you wrote.) An example of each is given.*

NOUN CLAUSE AS A SUBJECT	NOUN CLAUSE AS AN OBJECT
O. _What many claim_	O. _that two other men, John Vincent Atanasoff and Clifford Berry, were the legal inventors of the first electronic digital computer_
1. _____ _____	1. _____ _____

2 | AN INTERVIEW WITH JOHN MAUCHLY

Read these questions that a reporter might have asked John Mauchly. Use embedded questions and the words in parentheses to write Mauchly's responses.

0. Is your computer modeled after Atanasoff's computer? (It's difficult to say)

   It's difficult to say whether or not my computer is modeled after Atanasoff's computer.

1. How is your computer different from Atanasoff's computer? (I'm not sure)

   _____

2. How does Atanasoff's computer work? (I don't know)

   _____

3. Whose computer is better? (It's difficult to say)

   _____

4. When will you finish building your computer? (I don't know)

   _____

5. Does Atanasoff know that you are building a computer too? (It's questionable)

   _____

6. What does your computer look like? (It's difficult to say)

   _____

7. Does Atanasoff have a patent for his computer? (I don't know)

   _____

3 | A SUBSTITUTE TEACHER

You are a teacher, and you were out of town today. Your colleague Jim taught your class for you. You wonder what happened while you were gone. Use noun clauses and the words in parentheses to write embedded questions about what you'd like to ask Jim.

0. (want to ask / whether or not / students / behave in class)

   I want to ask Jim whether or not the students behaved in class.

1. (want to ask / who / miss class)

   _____

2. (want to ask / if / he / collect the homework from yesterday)

   _____

3. (wonder / how long / students / take to complete the reading activity)

   _____

4. (wonder / what / class / talk about during discussion time)

   _____

5. (wonder / what / he / tell students to do for homework)

   _____

6. (want to ask / where / he / put the key to my classroom)

   _____

7. (want to ask / whether or not / he / have fun teaching my class)

   _____

| 4 | EDITING: HOW DID ATANASOFF'S PATENT APPLICATION GET LOST? |

Read this note that a secretary in Professor Atanasoff's department might have left for another professor. There are five mistakes in the use of noun clauses. The first mistake is already corrected. Find and correct four more. (Note: There can be more than one way to correct a mistake.)

May 14, 1942

Dear Professor Costel:

What I left on your desk is a file that Professor Atanasoff gave me. You probably

know ~~the fact that~~ _{that} he left today for the East Coast. But did you know that he did leave a

lot of equipment in the basement? The equipment is crowding the basement is obvious. Please

advise on what should I do with it. I don't know I should throw it out. Also, please note that

he left some papers for you to sign. He said that they should go over to Beardshear Hall after

you have signed them so the patent application can be filed.

I'll see you when I return from vacation.

Best,

Joyce

Unit 22 Achievement Test

1 | LISTENING: EXIT POLLS

🎧 **A.** *Listen to this news report about exit polls. Complete the report by writing the word(s) that you hear. You will hear the recording two times.*

The results of the 2004 presidential election in the United States caused many doubts

about the accuracy of exit polls. On election night, exit polls predicted

_____*that one candidate would win*_____, yet when the actual votes were counted, a different
          0.

candidate turned out to be the winner. Because of this discrepancy, many U.S. citizens said they

had questions about how these polls worked. They _____ the
                                   1.

winner correctly.

In exit polls, voters are asked questions as they leave the places where they voted. Political

scientists _____ them make early estimates of election
                   2.

results. The polls can also provide other information. Political scientists

_____ who votes and what issues affect who they choose to
                3.

vote for.

After the actual results of the 2004 U.S. presidential election were known, political scientists

_____ much less accurate in this election than exit polls
               4.

typically are. One analyst said that the results were less predictive in part because of an

oversampling of women. He _____ to vote for the Democratic
                   5.

candidate. Analyst John Brown says, "Oversampling is a form of systematic error, which can

negatively affect the accuracy of the poll." He _____ to poll
                        6.

large numbers of randomly selected voters to avoid systematic errors.

Political scientists explain that systematic errors are different from random errors, such as

people forgetting who they voted for. They also _____ reduce
                           7.

systematic errors and give more accurate predictions. Finally, John Brown says, "People need to

remember that exit polls are only estimates of election results and that the actual winner of an

election is not decided by exit polls."

B. *Reread the news report about exit polls. Find two examples of indirect speech and one example of direct speech. Write them in the table below. (Note: Use only examples that are given in the passage. Do not use any examples that you wrote.) An example of each is given.*

INDIRECT SPEECH	DIRECT SPEECH

many U.S. citizens said they had questions O. <u>*about how these polls worked*</u>
 	
1. _____
 	
2. _____
 	
  _____
	Analyst John Brown says, "Oversampling is a form of systematic error, which can O. <u>*negatively affect the accuracy of the poll."*</u>
	
	1. _____
	
	  _____

---

2 | AN EXIT POLL INTERVIEW

Read this conversation between an exit poll interviewer and Daniel, a voter in the election. Use the words in parentheses to complete the indirect questions and statements.

Exit poll interviewer's questions:

Who did you vote for?
Are you completely satisfied with this candidate's policies?
What is the most important issue for you in this election?
What other issue could affect your vote?
Will you vote in the next election?

Daniel's responses:

Matthew Long.
No.
Funding for higher education.
Environmental policies.
Yes.

0. The exit poll interviewer asked Daniel _____ *who he had voted for* _____ .
   (who / vote for)

1. The exit poll interviewer asked Daniel _____ with that
   (if / completely satisfied)
   candidate's policies.

2. The exit poll interviewer asked Daniel _____ for him in
   (what / most important issue)
   this election.

3. Daniel stated _____ for him in this election.
   (funding for higher education / most important issue)

4. Daniel said _____ his vote.
   (environmental policies / affect)

5. The exit poll interviewer asked Daniel _____ .
   (whether or not / vote in the next election)

PART VI

3 | A POLITICAL SCIENCE CLASS

A. *Read this classroom discussion between a professor and some of his students. Then complete the indirect speech that summarizes the discussion.*

PROF. WANG: Why do you think this year's exit polls did not correctly predict the winner of the election?

STUDENT 1: Well, I know someone who lied in the exit poll this year.

PROF. WANG: OK, but that would be a random error. It wouldn't affect the results one way or the other.

STUDENT 2: The fact that women usually vote earlier in the day may have affected these exit poll results.

STUDENT 3: And I think that early poll predictions influenced people who voted later in the day.

PROF. WANG: Ah, but most people decided who to vote for much earlier, so that can't be the reason. Does anyone else have an idea of why the early poll results were so inaccurate?

STUDENT 4: I think they polled the wrong people.

PROF. WANG: Now that's a good answer! If the places they chose to poll were not representative of the whole voting population, then that's a systematic error. And that can be a reason for differences between early exit polls results and actual election results.

0. Professor Wang asked the students why they _____*thought*_____ this year's exit polls hadn't

correctly predicted the winner of the election.

1. Student 1 said someone had lied on the exit poll. Professor Wang said that the situation

_____ be a random error and wouldn't affect the results.

2. Student 2 said that women usually _____ earlier in the day.

3. Student 2 said that women voting early _____ have affected the results of the

exit polls.

4. Student 3 said that he _____ early poll predictions had influenced later votes.

5. Professor Wang said that Student 3's idea _____ not be a reason for the

difference.

6. Professor Wang then asked _____ anyone else had an idea of why the early poll

results had been so inaccurate.

B. *Read these statements in direct speech from the rest of the class discussion. Is the suggested change to reported speech correct* **(C)** *or incorrect* **(I)**? *Circle the correct answer.*

Ⓒ I   0. Direct: Professor Wang asked the class, "What questions do you have?"

Reported: Professor Wang asked the class what questions they had.

C I   1. Direct: Student 5 asked, "How did they choose where to give the exit polls this year?"

Reported: Student 5 asked how did they choose where to give the exit polls this year.

C I   2. Direct: "Are exit polls held at every election in the United States?" Student 6 asked.

Reported: Student 6 asked if exit polls are held at every election in the United States.

C I   3. Direct: Student 7 asked, "Why are the exit polls so important?"

Reported: Student 7 asked why are the exit polls so important.

---

4 | EDITING: A LETTER TO PROFESSOR POLITICS

Read this letter to Professor Politics, a political science analyst. There are seven mistakes in the use of indirect speech. The first mistake is already corrected. Find and correct six more. (Note: There can be more than one way to correct a mistake.)

Dear Professor Politics,

I am very upset at how deceiving the early exit polls were during last week's election.

When I went to bed on election night, the newscaster ~~told~~ *said* that Matthew Long had the most

votes. When I woke up, my husband asked who I think had won the election. Of course, I

told him that yesterday the polls had said Long would win. Then he told me the newspaper

had reported Ron Black as the winner, not Long! At first I didn't believe him, so he said I

could read it here in the newspaper for myself. I asked him how well the exit polls from the

last election predict the winner. He said they hadn't been accurate either! My daughter asked

me what was the purpose of exit polls. I didn't know, so I want to ask whether or not should

I pay attention to them.

Sincerely,

Martha Smith

Part VIII Achievement Test

60 Items
Score: _____

1 | LISTENING: ISSUES IN HIGHER EDUCATION

🎧 **A.** *Listen to this news report about some issues in higher education. Complete the news report by writing the word(s) that you hear. You will hear the recording two times.*

___That higher education is important___ is evident in today's society, and the majority of

0.

parents in the United States _____ for their children to go to

1.

college. _____ in the U.S. is any schooling beyond high school.

2.

While students used to decide _____ to college, now the

3.

decision most students make is _____. This is largely because

4.

students today _____ a college education, and most of the

5.

best-paying positions certainly require a degree.

The fact that higher education is valued so highly puts a lot of pressure on students and

their families. For example, students' grades are very important and students

_____ very stressful. Students and parents must also

6.

consider how much college costs. Last year, many university students in the U.S.

_____ one important factor that determined

7.

_____ after high school. In addition, what to study in

8.

college is a big decision for students to make at a relatively young age.

Parents and teachers know that standardized testing is another source of anxiety for students.

In recent years, critics of standardized testing have _____

9.

a student's ability to succeed in universities accurately. This is

_____ at students' high school grades and extracurricular

10.

activities when considering their applications for admittance.

B. *Reread the news report. Find one noun clause used as a subject and one used as an object. Write them in the table below. (Note: Use only clauses that are given in the narrative. Do not use any clauses that you wrote.)*

NOUN CLAUSE AS A SUBJECT	NOUN CLAUSE AS AN OBJECT
O. <u>The fact that higher education is valued so highly</u>	O. <u>how much college costs</u>
1. _____	1. _____

---

2 │ TUITION COSTS ON THE RISE

Read this conversation about tuition increases. Then read the changes to indirect speech below. Is the suggested change to indirect speech correct (C) or incorrect (I)? Circle the correct answer.

TED: What does it mean that college tuition costs are going up?

ANN: In the United States, tuition is the money that students pay to go to colleges or universities. Last year when tuition increased, students paid the extra costs for their education.

TED: Why doesn't the government pay for higher education in the United States?

ANN: The government helps, but students still have to pay for part of their education.

TED: Will the government pay more if tuition goes up?

ANN: No one knows right now.

TED: How much will tuition go up this year?

ANN: There will be an 8 percent increase this fall semester.

C **Ⓘ** 0. Ted asked what does it mean that college tuition costs are going up.

C **I** 1. Ann said that tuition is the money students pay for higher education.

C **I** 2. Ann said that when tuition increased last year, students had paid the extra costs for their education.

C **I** 3. Ted asked why the government doesn't pay for higher education in the United States.

C **I** 4. Ann told that the U.S. government does help, but students still have to pay for part of their education.

C **I** 5. Ted asked whether or not the government will pay more if tuition goes up.

C **I** 6. Ann said that no one knew right then.

C **I** 7. Ted asked how much will tuition costs go up that year.

C **I** 8. Ann said that there would be an 8-percent increase that fall semester.

Name _____   Date _____

| 3 | TECHNICAL SCHOOLS AND UNIVERSITIES |

Read this conversation between Helen and Tran. Then complete Helen's account of the conversation with indirect speech forms.

HELEN: Hi, Todd. Long time, no see! Hey, what did you decide what to do after high school?

TRAN: I decided to go to a technical school.

HELEN: I know what a university is, but don't know what a technical school is.

TRAN: Well, a technical school trains you for a specific job, like how to be an electrician, a plumber, or a mechanic. I'm going to study to be a mechanic.

HELEN: The technical school sounds perfect for you. I'm sure you made the right decision.

TRAN: I hope so. My father went to the same school 20 years ago.

HELEN: Your father was a very good mechanic before he retired. Is that because of the school?

TRAN: Probably. For a long time it was the second-best school in the state for mechanics.

HELEN: Is the school still as good today?

TRAN: It's even better now. It's one of the best schools in the country for mechanics. Will you let me fix your car when I get done with school?

HELEN: I will!

HELEN: I asked Tran _____*if he had decided what to do*_____ after high school. He
                                          0.

told _____ to a technical school. I said
                            1.

_____ what a university was. However, I said
                  2.

_____ what a technical school was. Tran said
                  3.

_____ you for a specific job. He said that he was
                  4.

going to study to be a mechanic. I said _____ perfect
                                                                    5.

for him. I told Tran _____ he had made the right
                                      6.

decision. Tran said _____. He also told
                                  7.

_____ to the same school 20 years earlier. I told
                  8.

_____ a very good mechanic before he had retired.
                  9.

Then I asked him _____ of the school. Tran said it
                                  10.

probably was. He said _____ the second-best
                                      11.

school in the state for mechanics for a long time. I asked him

_____ still as good. He told
                  12.

_____ even better now and that it's one of the

                    13.

best schools in the country for mechanics. Tran asked me

_____ fix my car when he got done with school.

                    14.

I told _____!

                    15.

---

4 | MAKING DECISIONS

Read this conversation between Kara and her teacher, Mr. Stevens. Then complete the embedded questions below.

Mr. Stevens' questions:

Do you want to go to college?
What college are you planning to attend?
Why did you choose to go to Harvard?
How far is Harvard from home?
How often will you visit home?

Where will you live?
Who will be your roommate?
What do you want to study?
Why did you decide to study psychology?
Will you work while you study?
How will you pay for your education?
How many classes can you take each
    semester?
Which classes do you want to take the
    first semester?
Why did you choose these classes?

What other classes would you like to take?

Kara's answers:

Yes.
Harvard is my first choice.
Because of its good reputation.
Fifty miles.
On holidays. They are always good times to
    visit.
I'm going to live in the dorms.
I'm going to live with a girl from Kansas.
I'm going to study psychology.
I have always wanted to help people.
No. Working takes time away from studying.
I received a large scholarship.
Four classes is usually standard.

English, math, psychology, and history.

These are required courses for all first-year
    students.
Spanish and chemistry sound fun.

0. Mr. Stevens asked Kara ___*whether or not she wanted*___ to go to college. She said yes.

1. Mr. Stevens asked Kara _____ to attend. She told him that Harvard

   was her first choice.

2. Mr. Stevens asked Kara _____ to Harvard. She told him that it was

   because of its good reputation.

3. Mr. Stevens asked Kara _____ from home. She said that it is 50 miles

   from her home.

4. Mr. Stevens asked Kara _____. She said that holidays are always

   good times to visit.

5. Mr. Stevens asked Kara _____. She told him that she was going to live in the dorms.

6. Mr. Stevens asked Kara _____. She told him that she was going to live with a girl from Kansas.

7. Mr. Stevens asked Kara _____. She told him that she was going to study psychology.

8. Mr. Stevens asked Kara _____ to study psychology. She told him that she had always wanted to help people.

9. Mr. Stevens asked Kara _____ while she studied. She told him that working takes away time from studying.

10. Mr. Stevens asked Kara _____ for her education. She told him that she had received a large scholarship.

11. Mr. Stevens asked Kara _____ each semester. She told him that four classes is usually standard.

12. Mr. Stevens asked Kara _____ the first semester. She told him English, math, psychology, and history were on her schedule.

13. Mr. Stevens asked Kara _____ classes. She told him they are required courses for all first-year students.

14. Mr. Stevens asked Kara _____ to take. She said Spanish and chemistry sounded fun.

5 | EDITING: A LETTER HOME

Kara is now living in the dorms at college with her new roommate, Alice. Read this letter from Kara to her parents. There are 12 mistakes in the use of noun clauses. The first mistake is already corrected. Find and correct 11 more. (Note: There can be more than one way to correct a mistake.)

Dear Mom and Dad,

The first few weeks of the semester have been very busy. My classes are difficult, and how much I ~~do~~ study now is amazing. I didn't know how much would I have to read! The other day, Alice asked me if I did want to go to a movie, but I had a psychology test the next day, so I didn't go. I'm worried by that I haven't gotten the graded test back yet. I asked the professor when would we find out our grades. He told that he would give them to us soon.

Last time we talked, I asked you when could I get a computer of my own. It's hard to know a computer in the computer labs on campus will be free or not. I don't know how could anything be more frustrating than when there aren't any computers available. Alice said me that having her own computer helps her get her work done more quickly. A laptop would be nice is obvious. Then I could take it to class with me to take notes! Do you know how efficient would that be? Just think about it, OK?

Love,

Kara

PART IX Diagnostic Test

1 | LISTENING: COMMON SENSE

🎧 **A.** *Listen to Arnold talk to his psychologist, Dr. Carlson, about common sense.*
Complete the conversation by writing the word(s) that you hear. You will hear the recording two times.

ARNOLD: I'm sure I wouldn't have so many problems if I just _____*used*_____
0.
common sense!

DR. CARLSON: Why do you say that?

ARNOLD: Well, I'm not a young man anymore. But on vacation, I insisted on jumping off

a high cliff into a lake when I knew I shouldn't have. I knew that I

_____ hurt myself if I jumped, but I did it anyway. I mean,
1.

people _____ doing stuff like that if they're not careful! If I
2.

_____, I wouldn't have hurt my back. And had I not hurt
3.

my back, I wouldn't have missed work. If I hadn't missed work, I'd

_____ to pay my rent. Now, if I _____ my rent
4.   5.

soon, I might get evicted. I just wish I _____ about the
6.

consequences before I jumped off that cliff.

DR. CARLSON: So, you feel frustrated that all these bad things have happened to you, and you

wish you _____ common sense in that situation.
7.

ARNOLD: That's right.

DR. CARLSON: Yes. Had you thought about the consequences of your actions, those bad things

would never have happened. Arnold, I believe you're ready to make some serious

changes in your life. If so, I suggest you start by thinking before you act.

Otherwise, you will continue to have problems.

B. In the conversation in Exercise A, find one example of an implied condition and one example of an inverted condition. Write the sentences below. (Note: Only use sentences that are given in the conversation. Do not use any sentences with words that you wrote.)

0. (implied) *If so, I suggest you start by thinking before you act.* _____

1. (implied) _____

_____

2. (inverted) *And had I not hurt my back, I wouldn't have missed work.* _____

3. (inverted) _____

_____

---

2 | IF ONLY …

Read this conversation between Harvey and Diego about their wishes. Complete the conversation with the correct verb forms. Write the letter of the best answer on each line.

HARVEY: You know, if I ____c____ (**a. would listen b. listen c. had listened d. have listened**) to my
           0.
        stockbroker, I'd be rich.

DIEGO: How's that?

HARVEY: Well, you know that company Corenox? If I had bought stock in that company when
        my broker recommended it, I _____ (**a. am b. could be c. had been d. have been**) retired
                       1.
        by now. I might have agreed to buy if he _____ (**a. asked b. has asked c. would ask**
                               2.
        d. had asked) me the month before, but we had just bought our house when he called. I
        would have bought a lot of stock if I _____ (**a. had known b. have known c. know**
                               3.
        d. could know) it would go up so much. If only I _____ (**a. could listen b. have listened**
                               4.
        c. listened d. had listened) to him!

DIEGO: I know. I also wish I _____ (**a. had paid b. have paid c. pay d. could pay**) more attention
                       5.
        to my broker. My wife wishes I _____ (**a. take b. have taken c. had taken d. could have**
                             6.
        taken) his advice too! If I _____ (**a. have b. had c. had had d. will have**) some money to
                       7.
        invest when he calls again, I probably will. _____ (**a. Only if b. If only c. Had d. Unless**)
                                    8.
        we had more money to invest! What would you do, Harvey, if you _____ (**a. have**
                                    9.
        b. would have c. have had d. had) all the money you wanted?

HARVEY: Well, I _____ (a. had paid b. have paid c. would pay d. would have paid) off my house, of
           10.

course. Then I'd probably _____ (a. buy b. have bought c. would buy d. have had bought) a
           11.

boat and sail out into the ocean. But that would depend on my wife, Rosie. I wouldn't

go _____ (a. had it not been for b. unless c. otherwise d. without) her. I think she would go
   12.

with me, but _____ (a. unless b. if not c. without d. if so), I wouldn't even consider it. I
      13.

don't know how I could go on _____ (a. if not b. except for c. but for d. unless) her.
                14.

DIEGO: I hear ya! I feel the same way about my kids. If I don't spend time with them every day,

I _____ (a. would feel b. feel c. have felt d. felt) like something's missing.
  15.

3 | HEART ATTACK PREVENTION AND TREATMENT

*Read these sentences about how to prevent and treat a heart attack. Use the correct forms
of the words in parentheses to complete the sentences.*

0. Millions of people die every year from heart attacks. We

_____ *suggest that you learn more about* _____ heart attack prevention and treatment.
           (suggest / that / you / learn / more)

1. If you smoke, it is _____, since smoking
           (desirable / that / you / quit)

increases your chance of having a heart attack.

2. Exercise can help decrease the risk of having a heart attack. Many doctors are

_____ more.
(insist / that / their patients / exercise)

3. We _____ every day.
     (recommend / get / 30 minutes of exercise)

4. Weight is another factor that can affect heart attack risk. It is

_____ .
(necessary / that / you / maintain / a healthy weight)

5. Some doctors are _____ .
         (recommend / that / their patients / lose / weight)

6. It is _____ in case of a heart attack.
     (important / that / you / have / a plan)

7. It is _____ to call for emergency medical
     (essential / that / you / know / the number)

treatment.

8. If you feel pain in the chest, it is _____
   (crucial / that / you / call / for emergency medical treatment)
   immediately.

9. We _____ before calling for help.
   (recommend / that / you / not / wait / longer than five minutes)

10. It is _____ as soon as possible because many medications
    (desirable / that / you / get / help)
    are most effective in the early stages of a heart attack.

11. We _____, even if you are not sure that what you are
    (suggest / call / for / help)
    experiencing is a heart attack.

12. Don't drive yourself to the hospital if possible, but _____.
    (ask / that / someone / drive / you)

13. Doctors _____, rather than having to treat them.
    (prefer / that / their patients / prevent / heart attacks)

14. In most places, it is _____, even if
    (mandatory / for / hospital staff / give / you / emergency medical treatment)
    you don't have health insurance.

4 | LOST AND FOUND

Read Jen's account of her arrival in a foreign country. Complete the sentences with the correct form of each verb.

I knew I should have put my passport in my bag instead of in my pocket. When I arrived at the airport, I was asked to show my passport, but I couldn't find it! So I told the immigration officer that I had taken it with me on the plane and that maybe I had left it there. I had to wait for two hours while the cleaning crew looked for my passport. Well, one of them finally found it, but by that time, I had missed my connecting flight, so I had to get a hotel for the night. Meanwhile, my address book was in my luggage, so I couldn't call my host family who was waiting for me at the airport!

0. Jen wishes that she _____*had put*_____ her passport in her bag.
   (put)

1. If she had done that, the whole mess _____.
   (not happen)

2. Jen wouldn't have put her passport in her pocket if she _____ she
   (know)

   was going to lose it.

3. Immigration officers cannot allow people out of the airport if they

   _____ their passports.
   (not see)

4. Anyone could enter the country if the immigration officers _____
   (not do)

   their jobs.

5. If the cleaning crew hadn't found her passport, Jen _____ back in her
   (be)

   own country right now, trying to get a new passport.

6. Had the cleaning crew _____ honest, Jen might never have gotten her
   (not be)

   passport back.

7. If only everyone _____ so honest!
   (be)

8. Jen would call to thank the person who found her passport if she

   _____ who the person was.
   (know)

9. If Jen hadn't lost her passport, she _____ her connecting flight.
   (make)

10. If Jen had made her connecting flight, she _____ to stay overnight in
    (not need)

    a hotel.

11. If only Jen _____ her address book with her on the plane!
    (bring)

12. Jen's host family _____ home if they had known about the situation.
    (stay)

13. Jen wishes she _____ those mistakes.
 (not make)

14. If Jen _____ again, she'll make sure to know exactly where her
 (fly)

passport is.

---

5 | EDITING: E-MAIL HOME

Read Jen's e-mail to her family back home. There are eight mistakes in the use of verb forms. The first mistake is already corrected. Find and correct seven more. (Note: There can be more than one way to correct a mistake.)

Dear Mom and Dad,

       known
I just arrived to my new home, and I'm exhausted. Had I ~~know~~ that I would have so much trouble getting here, I would have done things differently. First of all, I put my passport in my pocket instead of in my bag, and I lost it! Dad, I know you recommended me not to keep it there, but did I listen? No! Had not I put my passport in my pocket, I could have avoided a big mess. When I got off the plane, the immigration officer asked that I showed him my passport. But I couldn't find it anywhere! I was so nervous because the officer wouldn't let me through without it. Hadn't I lost my passport, I wouldn't have missed my connecting flight. Also, if I were thinking, I would have taken my host family's number with me. Were I to call them, they wouldn't have gone to the airport to get me. Were I to do it all over again, I will definitely be more careful.

Love,

Jen

Unit 23 Achievement Test

1 | LISTENING: INTUITION

🎧 *A. Listen to the radio interview. Complete the interview by writing the word(s) that you hear. You will hear the recording two times.*

DIANA MORKEN: Welcome back to our show, *Mind and Body.* My next guest is Dr. Anthony Kapp, a psychologist who has just written a new book, *Listening to Your Intuition.* Dr. Kapp, welcome.

DR. KAPP: Thank you, Diana.

MORKEN: Dr. Kapp, in your book, you talk about intuition. Tell me about that.

KAPP: Well, intuition refers to understanding or knowing something because of a feeling rather than by considering the facts. If a person _____has_____ an
0.
idea about what is true or correct in a certain situation without having logical reasons for the idea, that's intuition. In other words, intuition means that you

_____ what you should do in a given situation even if you can't
1.

explain why. I believe that if we all _____ more attention to our
2.

intuitive feelings, we would do better in life.

MORKEN: Can you give us an example?

KAPP: Sure. Let's say you're looking for a job. You wish you _____
3.

something that you're really excited about. Then you are offered a position

that seems perfect for you, and at first you're really excited. But a little later

you get a feeling that you shouldn't take the job, even though you don't

really know why. So you start to worry: If you don't take that job,

_____ another one? You convince yourself that if you don't
4.

accept the job, you'll wish you _____. So you take the job. Three
5.

months later, you realize that you've made a mistake. You don't enjoy your

work. Of course, you wouldn't have taken the job if you had had a logical reason not to. But you didn't have a real reason. And now you think, "If only I had listened to my intuition! If I hadn't taken this job, I _____
6.
doing something that I loved right now." In that situation, you could have gotten a better job if you had paid attention to your feelings.

MORKEN: So you're saying if you _____ your intuition, you wouldn't be in
7.
this situation.

KAPP: Exactly, so pay attention to what your intuition tells you!

B. *Reread the example given by Kapp. Find three sentences with past unreal conditionals. Write them below. (Note: Only use sentences that are given in the example. Do not use any words that you wrote.) An example is given.*

0. *Of course, you wouldn't have taken the job if you had had a logical reason not to.*

1. _____

2. _____

| 2 | **WISHES** |

Read each sentence. Then write the letter of the sentence that is closest in meaning to the original sentence.

___a___ 0. If only I weren't so forgetful.
    a. I forget a lot of things.
    b. I remember most things.
    c. I had a good memory before.

_____ 1. I don't want you to buy that car.
    a. I wish you wouldn't buy that car.
    b. I wish you didn't buy that car.
    c. I wish you hadn't bought that car.

_____ 2. My wife wants me to help her more with yard work.
    a. My wife wishes I had helped her more with yard work.
    b. My wife wishes I helped her more with yard work.
    c. My wife wishes I had not been so busy so I could help her with yard work.

_____ 3. My brother took a job, and now he's really unhappy about it.
    a. My brother wishes he wouldn't take the job.
    b. My brother wishes he didn't take the job.
    c. My brother wishes he hadn't taken the job.

_____ 4. His parents are not happy that he quit college.
  a. His parents wish he didn't quit college.
  b. His parents wish he hadn't quit college.
  c. His parents wish he wouldn't quit college.
_____ 5. They are sorry that they went out of town.
  a. They wish they didn't go out of town.
  b. They wish they hadn't gone out of town.
  c. They wish they wouldn't go out of town.

3 | HOME-BASED BUSINESS

Read this Internet advertisement for a home-based business. Complete the advertisement by writing the correct form of each verb. Some items may have more than one correct answer.

If you _____*would like*_____ to earn $15,000 to $20,000 per month, then keep reading.
           0. (like)

    Do you ever imagine all the things you _____ if you didn't have to
                      1. (do)

work so much? Do you ever think how your life _____ if you made a lot
                      2. (change)

of money? If you _____ all the time and money in the world, what
             3. (have)

would your life be like? Take a moment to think about these questions. Dreams like these

_____ true if you don't make them happen. If you want to have more
        4. (not come)

free time *and* make hundreds of thousands of dollars per year, you _____
                                5. (want)

to take advantage of this simple home-based business. This isn't a typical get-rich-quick scheme

that promises you a fortune without working for it. It's a legitimate business, and you are paid

only if you _____. But if you _____ the easy
          6. (work)   **7. (follow)**

system, you'll be on your way to a lifestyle beyond your wildest dreams. Face it, you

_____ to read this if you hadn't been looking for something more in life.
    8. (not start)

You wouldn't have read this far if you _____ that this opportunity might
                      9. (not think)

be for you. Stop thinking, "If only I _____ so busy" or "If only I
                      10. (am not)

_____ more money." Take action now to change your life! <u>Click here</u> to
    11. (have)

learn more about this incredible business opportunity.

4 | EDITING: UNCERTAIN FUTURE

Read this conversation between college roommates. There are five mistakes in the use of verb forms. The first mistake is already corrected. Find and correct four more. (Note: There can be more than one way to correct a mistake.)

MIKE: So, would you be really excited if you ~~would get~~ that job in Washington?
 got

JOSH: Yeah, I would love that job, but I haven't heard from them. I shouldn't have waited so long to send in the forms. I might have heard from them by now if I applied earlier.

MIKE: What are you doing if you don't find a job before graduation?

JOSH: If I won't get a job, I'll have to move back home for a while. I'd be so much less stressed right now if I know that I was going to get a job soon!

Unit 24 Achievement Test

1 | LISTENING: DEAR GABBY

🎧 **A.** *Listen to this excerpt from* The Dear Gabby Show *with therapist Dr. Gabriela VanDeren. Complete the transcript by writing the word(s) that you hear. You will hear the recording two times.*

GABBY: Welcome to *The Dear Gabby Show*. Today I have a letter from Frank in Ohio. He has a

problem that's pretty common. Frank's letter says:

FRANK: *Dear Gabby, My brother-in-law owes my wife and me some money. He*

_____asked_____ that we lend him $2,000 last year as a business loan. At first, I
                0.

_____ that he go to a bank for the money, but he said the bank had
              1.

already turned him down. So had all his friends. He had to borrow the money from

someone. Otherwise, he wouldn't have been able to start his own business. So, my wife

insisted on _____ him out and loaning him the money, and I agreed. It's
                    2.

been a year now, and I've requested that he _____ paying us back, but
                                                         3.

he hasn't. It's a difficult situation, and I wonder what you would recommend I

_____.
          4.

GABBY: Well listen, Frank, the first thing I suggest _____ is talking to your
                                                                  5.

brother-in-law. Show him that you want to work with him towards a solution. Tell him

you are proposing that the money _____ back little by little. In fact, if
                                           6.

_____ you, I'd make up a plan for him to start paying you back, even if
         7.

it's just 20 dollars per week. With such a plan, you'll start getting your money back

immediately. When you talk to him, I'd recommend that you _____
                                                                       8.

anything from him. Otherwise, he might not listen to you at all. Good luck. Stay with

us, you're listening to *The Dear Gabby Show*.

B. In the paragraph of Gabby's suggestion, find two examples of implied conditions and write them below. (Note: Use only sentences that are given in Gabby's suggestion. Do not use any sentences with words that you wrote.)

0. _Otherwise, he wouldn't have been able to start his business._____

1. _____

2. _____

2 | MORE ADVICE FROM DR. GABBY

Dr. Gabby summarizes her ideas and gives Frank a few more tips. Complete the sentences. Use the correct forms of the appropriate verbs from the box.

ask	~~deal~~	forget	pay	sign	talk
behave	explain	invite	see	stay	work

0. It's important that you _____ deal _____ with this situation immediately.

1. It is reasonable that you _____ for your money back.

2. It's advisable that you _____ to your brother-in law as soon as possible.

3. It's critical to _____ the problem clearly to him.

4. It's important that you _____ calm when you talk to him, so your brother-in-law doesn't get angry.

5. It's advisable that you _____ together on a solution.

6. It's necessary for your brother-in-law to _____ like a grown-up.

7. It's essential that he _____ you back, even if it's just $20 per week.

8. In the future, it is advisable that you _____ a written agreement with a person before lending him or her money.

3 | BEST ACTOR

Actor Julian Hales has won an award for best actor. Read these sentences from his acceptance speech. Rewrite each underlined word or phrase with an if *clause that restates the condition. (Note: There may be more than one way to rewrite some words or phrases.)*

0. <u>Had I known</u> I would win, I would have prepared something to say.

If I had known _____

1. <u>Were I better prepared</u>, I would have a list of everyone that I want to acknowledge. I hope I don't forget anyone!

_____

2. First I would like to thank my manager, Tim Fathera. <u>But for him</u>, I wouldn't be standing here now.

_____

3. Next I'd like to thank Bruce Cochran, who directed the film. Bruce was a great director. <u>Without him</u>, the film wouldn't have become such a masterpiece.

_____

4. Bruce worked some long hours. <u>Should he win</u> an award tonight, he'll deserve it.

_____

5. Do you know Bruce's films have won 30 awards? <u>With a little luck</u>, he'll win 30 more.

_____

6. <u>If so</u>, don't forget your old friends, all right, Bruce?

_____

7. I also want to thank Mark Wolf, my accent coach. <u>Were it not for him</u>, I'd never have gotten the accent right.

_____

8. Maybe they'll have an award for you later tonight, Mark. <u>If not</u>, you can borrow mine anytime you want.

_____

9. Last but not least, I want to thank my wife, Julie. <u>Had you not supported me</u>, I never could have done any of this.

_____

| 4 | **EDITING: CARPET CLEANING** |

Jim just arrived home from work. Read his conversation with his wife, Diane. There are four mistakes in the use of verb forms. The first mistake is already corrected. Find and correct three more. (Note: There can be more than one way to correct a mistake.)

JIM: Hi, Honey. Why is the couch in the kitchen?

DIANE: I spilled juice on the carpet this morning, so I called the carpet cleaners and asked that

come

someone ~~came~~ right away. The guy recommended that I moved the couch before he got

here, so I had to move it all by myself.

JIM: I'm sorry. I would have helped you if I were home.

DIANE: That's OK. So he cleaned the carpet, but he suggested us to stay off it until tomorrow

morning.

Part IX Achievement Test

1 | LISTENING: STUDENT PROBLEMS

🎧 **A.** *Listen to the conversation between two college roommates. Complete the
conversation by writing the word(s) that you hear. You will hear the recording two times.*

NANCY: I wouldn't be doing so badly in college if I ____had followed____ my true interests!
0.

MICHELLE: What do you mean?

NANCY: Well, when I first got here, I took a test to see what kind of job I might be good at.

The test showed that if I liked people, which I do, then I _____ great
1.

as a hotel manager. I was surprised, because I had never thought about a career in

management. I wanted to go into music. But lots of musicians _____
2.

much money if they're not incredibly talented. So I thought I'd try hotel

management. But I don't really like it. If I _____ music, I wouldn't
3.

have had such a hard time with my classes last year. And were I not getting such bad

grades, I wouldn't have lost my scholarship. If I hadn't lost my scholarship, I

_____ work. Now, if I _____, I can't pay for tuition.
4.   **5.**

I just wish I _____ my love of music!
6.

MICHELLE: I'm sorry, Nancy. I wish I _____ about this earlier. Had I known, I
7.

would have tried to help.

NANCY: Thanks.

MICHELLE: It can be hard to study something without loving it. And I know *I'd* rather be poor

and happy than rich and miserable. It's never too late to change your mind, you

know. Lots of people change their majors in college. Why don't you? Otherwise, you

might be unhappy for the rest of your life!

B. In the conversation in Exercise A, find one example of an implied condition and one example of an inverted condition. Write the sentences below. (Note: Use only sentences that are given in the conversation. Do not use any sentences with words that you wrote.)

0. (implied) *It can be hard to study something without loving it.* _____

1. (implied) _____

   _____

2. (inverted) *And were I not getting such bad grades, I wouldn't have lost my scholarship.* _____

3. (inverted) _____

   _____

2	**TWENTY YEARS LATER**

Read the conversation between Nancy and Michelle, 20 years later. Complete the conversation with the correct verb forms. Write the letter of the best answer on each line.

NANCY: I'm so glad I took your advice and changed my major in college. If I ____*a*____
          0.

(a. hadn't   b. haven't   c. didn't   d. not), I wouldn't be where I am now.

MICHELLE: How's that?

NANCY: Well, do you remember that I was studying hotel management and how much I

hated it? If I hadn't changed my major to music, I _____ (a. will be   b. would be
                                                          1.

c. had been   d. have been) so unhappy. I might have continued with hotel management if

I _____ (a. haven't talked   b. wouldn't talk   c. hadn't talked   d. didn't talk) to you. If I had
    2.

known that I'd be running a profitable music store now, I _____ (a. would never
                                                          3.

give   b. had never given   c. would never have given   d. will never give) a second thought to

majoring in music. If only I _____ (a. learned   b. would learn   c. had learned   d. did learn)
                              4.

earlier to follow my heart!

MICHELLE: That's great, Nancy! I still wish I _____ (a. had done   b. would do   c. have done   d. do)
5.

what I loved, but I always worried that I wasn't good enough at painting to make

any money. I wish I _____ (a. could   b. will   c. might   d. have) just let go of my fears! If
6.

I ever have enough money to take a year off and paint full time, I _____ (a. would
7.

b. would have to   c. could   d. am going to) do it! _____ (a. Only if   b. If only   c. Otherwise
8.

d. Unless) I didn't have to work for money! Would you be running your store if you

_____ (a. wouldn't have to   b. won't have to   c. don't have to   d. didn't have to) work?
9.

NANCY: Oh, I don't know. I like running the store, but if I didn't need the money, I guess I

_____ (a. recorded   b. would record   c. had recorded   d. could have recorded) my own music,
10.

even if no one would buy it. I _____ (a. might also travel   b. had also traveled   c. must
11.

also travel   d. also traveled) more. Of course, I _____ (a. didn't go   b. won't go   c. hadn't
12.

gone   d. wouldn't go) without Rob. I think he would go with me, but _____ (a. unless
13.

b. if not   c. without   d. if so), I might just listen to music all day! I don't know what I'd do

_____ (a. except for   b. unless   c. if not   d. without) music.
14.

MICHELLE: I know! If I _____ (a. can't paint   b. couldn't paint   c. didn't paint   d. hadn't painted)
15.

something at least once a week, I feel incomplete.

3 | AVOIDING AND PREPARING FOR FIRES

Read these sentences about how to avoid and prepare for a fire. Use the correct forms of the words in parentheses to complete the sentences.

0. Thousands of people die every year in fires. We ____*suggest that you learn*____ how
   (suggest / that / you / learn)

   to avoid and prepare for fires where you live and work.

1. It is _____.
   (important / that / you / have / an evacuation plan)

2. We _____ every few months.
   (suggest / that / you / have / a fire drill)

3. It is _____ as quickly as possible.
   (necessary / that / you / leave / a burning building)

4. Don't call the emergency number from your home if it is on fire. Use a cell phone or

   _____ instead.
   (ask / that / a neighbor / call / for you)

5. It is _____ in a fire to avoid inhaling smoke.
   (essential / that / you / stay/ low to the floor)

6. The fire department _____ out of each building.
   (insist / that / local businesses / identify/ multiple exits)

7. It is _____ with working batteries in your home.
   (crucial / that / you / have / smoke detectors)

8. It is _____ in the buildings they own.
   (mandatory / that / landlords / provide / working smoke detectors)

9. It is _____ near the kitchen.
   (important / that / you / keep / a fire extinguisher)

10. Some home owners are _____.
    (insist / that / their upper-floor windows / equip / with escape ladders)

11. We _____ to make sure they are not overloaded.
    (recommend / check / electrical outlets)

12. If you smoke, it is _____.
    (desirable / that / you / never / smoke / in bed)

13. In fact, we _____ at all.
    (recommend / that / you / not smoke / in the house)

14. Insurance companies _____ about your home,
    (prefer / that / you / have / updated information)

    including current photographs of any valuables in the home.

4 | RUNNING OUT OF GAS

Read Eric's account of running out of gas. Complete the sentences with the correct form of each verb.

I should have filled up my car with gas last night, but I forgot. Then, on my way to work this morning, I ran out of gas! It took about 20 minutes before someone stopped to help me. A woman gave me a ride to a gas station. I would have called my office from there, but I couldn't remember the number, and the gas station didn't have a phone book. But here's the worst part: I was supposed to give a presentation first thing in the morning. Everyone was waiting for me for half an hour before I finally got there. By then it was too late to give the presentation, and I had to explain the situation to my manager.

0. Eric wishes he _____*had filled*_____ up his car with gas last night.
   (fill)

1. If he had done so, he _____ late to work.
   (not be)

2. Eric _____ to fill his car with gas if he had known he was going to
   (not forget)

   run out.

3. If the woman _____ him up, Eric would probably have been fired by
   (not pick)

   now.

4. He _____ the woman a thank-you note if he knew her address.
   (send)

5. Without her, Eric _____ to work before 10:00.
   (not get)

6. If only everyone _____ so nice!
   (be)

7. If Eric hadn't run out of gas, he _____ on time to give his
   (arrive)

   presentation.

8. If he had been to work on time, he _____ to talk with his manager.
   (not need)

9. If only Eric _____ his work number!
   (learn)

10. If Eric had called his office, he _____ half an hour of everyone's
    (not waste)

    time.

11. Eric wishes he _____ the mistake of running out of gas.
    (not make)

12. If Eric is low on gas again, he _____ to fill up.
    (remember)

13. Obviously, a car can't run if it _____ empty.
    (be)

14. The whole country would probably come to a stop if we all _____
    (run)

    out of gas.

5 | EDITING: E-MAIL ABOUT THE DAY

Read Eric's e-mail to his girlfriend. There are eight mistakes in the use of verb forms. Find and correct seven more. The first mistake is already corrected. (Note: There can be more than one way to correct a mistake.)

Dear Kara,

      I just got home, and I'm exhausted. Had I ~~know~~ *known* that I was going to have such a bad day, I would have stayed in bed. First of all, I forgot to fill up my car with gas last night, so I ran out of gas this morning on the way to work! I was hurrying because I had to give a presentation. Had not I been in such a hurry, I would have stopped to get gas. When I finally arrived at work half an hour late, my manager asked that I spoke to him. He said it was too late to give my presentation. Hadn't I been late, I would have been able to give it. He recommended me to write a formal apology to my colleagues. Also, if I were thinking, I would have learned my work number a long time ago. Were I to call the office, my colleagues wouldn't have had to waste half an hour waiting for me. Were I to start the day over again, I will definitely be more careful.

Love,

Eric

Audioscript

PART I Diagnostic Test

Erin Henderson has been creating music since she was five. Although her name may be unfamiliar to you, people around the world recognize her voice. She has released seven albums, and she is preparing to release her eighth album, *Family of Man,* this week. Her unique style carefully combines elements of African and European music. She began recording her new album in a studio, but in the end, she recorded most of the songs in an empty swimming pool. As you listen to the album, you'll hear birds in the background, and, in one song, a plane is flying overhead. Some of the songs will make you dance, while others will relax you.

Before she started work on *Family of Man,* Henderson had taken some time off from songwriting to travel to the Far East. Her travels have influenced her music for the better. As you listen to *Family of Man,* you'll realize how many changes she has made in her style. She used to rely heavily on instrumentation in her music. Now, she uses fewer instruments, which focuses the listener on her voice. I believe this is her finest work yet.

Unit 1 Achievement Test

It's early in the morning in the heart of the Amazonian rainforest. Toucans are calling to each other. Monkeys are playing in the trees. A tourist is walking down an overgrown trail, stopping from time to time to take in the exotic sights and sounds of the jungle.

Do you wish that tourist was you? Well, imagine that your dream has come true. You've booked a ticket for the Amazon Adventure Tour. Look at your exciting itinerary! You land in Manaus, Brazil, at 10 A.M. on Sunday, and you arrive at your luxurious hotel overlooking the Amazon River at 1 P.M. As soon as you check in, you'll start to relax. During your week-long stay at the hotel, you'll have the time of your life! With river cruises and trips to local villages on the itinerary, by the end of your vacation, you'll have experienced the magic of the Amazon!

My name is Donna, and I'm a travel agent. Whether your dream destination is the Amazon or some other exotic locale, I'll work with you to plan the perfect vacation! I've been helping people like you to plan their dream vacations for more than 20 years, so call me today!

Unit 2 Achievement Test

Jim Reed first met his wife, Nancy, on a stage while hundreds of people were watching. Jim used to sing in a rock-and-roll band. Nancy, a local artist, liked Jim and had been going to his shows regularly. Then one night, the drummer didn't show up. After Jim had sung a couple of songs without the drummer, he jokingly asked the audience if anyone wanted to come up and play the drums for the rest of the show. Nancy didn't know how to play the drums, but she wasn't going to pass up the opportunity to meet Jim. So she volunteered to play and took a seat behind the drums. The noise she made wasn't pretty. Fortunately, she had only played for a couple of minutes when the real drummer arrived. It turned out that Jim liked Nancy, even though she was a terrible drummer. After they had dated for a few months, Jim decided to propose the same way they had met—in front of a large audience. Jim had it all planned: He would ask Nancy to come on stage, then he would propose to her. However, Nancy had heard ahead of time what Jim was planning to do, so while Jim was still outside, she told the audience and gave them confetti. When Jim proposed to Nancy, the audience surprised him with the confetti! Jim and Nancy were married later that year.

Unit 3 Achievement Test

When I was little, I watched hours of television every day. Unfortunately, the time that I wasted sitting in front of the television could have been put to better use by playing outside or learning a skill.

I believe that watching television has harmful effects on a person's health and mind. First of all, television negatively affects people's health. We all know that exercise is good for our health. However, many people prefer to sit and eat junk food while watching TV. If you do this for many years, the lack of activity will probably begin to make you feel bad. You probably won't have much energy, and you might gain weight.

In addition, there is research that shows that people who watch TV for many hours per day have lower IQs than people who read.

To conclude, if you care about your physical and mental health, turn off your TV!

PART I Achievement Test

Sean Collins has been acting in movies since he was 12. Although his name may be unfamiliar to you, people around the world know his face. He has appeared in seven movies, and is working on his eighth film, *Homeless*. His unique acting style artistically combines the characteristics of a tough gangster with those of a sensitive lover. He started his acting career on Broadway as a child, but since then he has done more acting in Hollywood. As you watch him, you'll notice a greater depth to his acting than he showed in his earlier films. Fans are betting that this film will earn him an Academy Award. Some of the scenes will leave you breathless, while others will move you.

Before he began work on *Homeless*, Collins had spent some time at home with his wife and his new baby. His time off has changed him for the better. As you watch *Homeless*, you'll understand the changes that have occurred in his acting style. He used to use mostly his voice and grand gestures. Now, he acts with fewer gestures; instead, he relies on subtle facial expressions to reveal his character's emotions. I think this is his finest film yet.

PART II Diagnostic Test

DOUG: That's an amazing painting, isn't it?

LIZA: It is amazing! The artist must have worked on it for years. You've got to get a picture of it!

DOUG: We're not supposed to take pictures of the paintings. But we should look in the gift shop when we're done. They might have a print of this painting. Most museums do sell prints of their most popular paintings. At least the museums that I've been to. Look at the date of the painting. When you first looked at it, you might have thought it was painted from a photograph. I know I did. But it wasn't. It was painted before the camera was invented. Incredible, isn't it?

LIZA: It is! What kind of paint do you think he used? It couldn't have been regular oil paint. I've never seen anything like it.

DOUG: Neither have I. And I even studied art like this in college.

LIZA: So did I! You know, I'm afraid we may not be able to find a print in the gift shop. Maybe we could take a picture after all. We don't have to take the picture with the flash. Do you think we could?

DOUG: We'd better not. We might get into trouble.

Unit 4 Achievement Test

MRS. PARK: I just love packing. Don't you?

MR. PARK: Are you joking? Not at all!

MRS. PARK: Well, I really do. I've always enjoyed packing. Oh, I know it's a lot of work, but I do enjoy going through all my things and putting them in boxes. By the way, have you seen the tape? I want to tape this box.

MR. PARK: No, I haven't. I hope you realize that you have about three times as many clothes as I do. Don't you think you should give away whatever you don't wear?

MRS. PARK: You're right. Maybe I should get rid of one of these jackets. Let's see, the red one is new, but so is the blue one. The red one is nice to wear to work, but the blue one is too. I like that the red one doesn't have any buttons on the sleeves, but neither does the blue one. I just don't know. I wear them both.

MR. PARK: What about these dresses? Let's see, you do wear this flowery one, but I've never seen you wear this brown one.

MRS. PARK: It is ugly, isn't it? I guess I could get rid of it. Let's start a box of things to give away.

MR. PARK: I think I've changed my mind. I do like packing!

Unit 5 Achievement Test

DALE: So that's the restaurant. Do you like it?

SANDY: I love it! But shouldn't you have put in some smoke detectors?

DALE: They should have installed them yesterday, but they never showed up. They're supposed to come tomorrow. I ought to call and remind them about it. I mustn't forget.

SANDY: Also, I was thinking you could have different lighting. For instance, you might consider using some nice lamps instead of these fluorescent lights.

DALE: I agree, but I'm renting the building, and I'm not supposed to make changes to the lighting. We're not allowed to, according to the contract.

SANDY: You don't have to take out the lights. You could just keep them off and use the lamps instead.

DALE: That's a good idea. I ought to have talked to you earlier!

Unit 6 Achievement Test

MRS. JENSEN: I'm worried. Where could Nora be? She couldn't still be at work. Something must be wrong!

MR. JENSEN: You're right. She can't be at work now. It's almost seven o'clock. But she might have just gone somewhere after work. She should be home soon.

MRS. JENSEN: She must have tried to call us. She always calls us if she's late! Her cell phone may not be working, so she may not have been able to call, but where might she be, and why couldn't she have called from another phone? She may be hurt!

MR. JENSEN: I don't know, but it's no use worrying. She might not be in any danger at all. She could have run into an old friend and started talking. She should call or be home any minute now.

PART II Achievement Test

ERIC: This mall has gotten old, hasn't it?

KELLY: It has gotten old! It has to have been one of the first malls ever built. They really must improve it if they want more business.

ERIC: You're right. Aren't you supposed to buy a gift for your dad's birthday?

KELLY: Yeah. The department store could have the tool set he's been looking for. We ought to go take a look. They may not have exactly what he wants, but I saw an advertisement for something like what he was looking for. At least I think I did.

ERIC: Watch that hole in the floor! You could have fallen in it! That other lady almost fell in it too. It was pure luck that she didn't. I think we should tell an employee that they need to cover the hole, don't you?

KELLY: Yes, I do! The mall staff must not be aware of it. I'm just amazed no one has fallen in it yet.

ERIC: So am I. You know, the other day I read an article about all the problems with public safety in places like this. Most people don't seem to worry much about how dangerous these places can be, but I do.

KELLY: So do I! I'm afraid the staff here in the mall might not do anything about the hole. No one seems to care about this place, and someone might get hurt. We don't have to tolerate it. I might e-mail someone on the city council about this when I get home.

ERIC: Good idea. I will too. They shouldn't be allowed to stay open like this.

PART III Diagnostic Test

Have you hugged a dog today? Have you pet a cat? Central City Animal Shelter has many pets that need the love and attention of a new owner and friend. The cats and dogs at our shelter have been displaced and need loving new homes. For many people, owning a pet can be one of life's greatest experiences. By adopting a pet, you'll be giving one of these animals a second chance, and the animal you take home may truly become your best friend. Each animal up for adoption is healthy and disease free. We're conveniently located just east of Central Park. Come visit us today.

Unit 7 Achievement Test

Welcome to Chemistry 101. My name is Dr. Smith. This semester you will experiment with oxygen, hydrogen, air, electricity, sugar, and energy, as well as other natural phenomena. You will also learn Mendeleev's periodic table of elements. A course project is required, but you will have some freedom to choose your own topics. Students are expected to be in their seats when the bell rings and to hand in homework assignments on time. I hope we'll have some fun this semester.

Unit 8 Achievement Test

Welcome to Science and Society. The development of technology relies on previous knowledge, discoveries, and inventions. For example, one of the greatest inventions in the world is the Internet. However, the Internet couldn't exist without knowing about electricity and the computer first. Another example is the cell phone, which uses previous inventions such as batteries, the telephone, and the radio. No one knows what the next big invention will be. It could be a machine that transports you across the globe within seconds, much like a fax machine! On today's show, we'll be looking at the future of technology.

Unit 9 Achievement Test

I love paper. I probably have enough paper on my desk to cover the walls of my house. So I was a little concerned when I heard some talk about making our office paperless. Many offices are becoming paperless, which means using and wasting fewer papers. But do any of these offices really work? According to Howard Foster, an office managing consultant, a great many of these so-called paperless offices are not really paperless at all. For example, you might think that e-mail reduces the need for paper. But Foster claims that most offices actually increase their quantity of printing after getting e-mail connections. The increased amount of information that people receive creates more demand for the information in its familiar black-and-white, portable form. In addition, paperless offices require a great deal of ongoing training to keep information from getting lost in cyberspace. Foster thinks that paperless offices are both possible and efficient. But he points out that the system takes some getting used to, especially for people like me.

Unit 10 Achievement Test

Come visit the historic Ackerly Mansion. Located in the heart of charming downtown Minneapolis, the newly reopened Ackerly Mansion is an artistic jewel of the Midwest. Guided tours are offered daily from 10 A.M. to 4 P.M., Monday through Saturday. As a special event, Edward Ackerly's granddaughter, Susan Mann, will share personal family stories and photographs this Saturday from 12 to 2. You'll learn more about the exciting, colorful past of the Ackerly family and about their far-reaching influence on the early pioneer history of Minneapolis. Following the story telling, fresh muffins and homemade ice cream will be served in the mansion's spacious guest parlor, and there will be a band and dancing in the music hall. For more information, call 555-2672.

PART III Achievement Test

Did you take a vitamin today? Are you one of the millions of people who take nutritional supplements? Nutritional supplements are a multi-billion dollar industry, and now you can get your share of the sales by owning your own home-based Nutri store. For a great many people, running a business from home is an extremely profitable enterprise. We're talking about a lot of money here, so take advantage of this exciting new opportunity. Call now and receive a free video that describes the business that has made thousands of people wealthy beyond their wildest dreams. Every caller within the next 10 minutes will also receive a "Healthy Living Pac" absolutely free. Call now!

PART IV Diagnostic Test

The Lumière brothers, working in their father's photographic film factory, invented the first working movie camera. The contributions they made to film were significant. It was 1895 when they produced the movie camera, a non-working prototype of which was brought to them from New York by their father, a wealthy manufacturer. The prototype, which cost nearly a million dollars in today's money, drove the brothers to develop a more inexpensive version of the movie camera. When the camera was complete, the first movie, directed by the Lumière brothers themselves, showed their father's workers walking out of the factory, the same factory that the brothers worked in, at the end of the day. Another part of the film, starring their father's gardener being sprayed in the face with a hose, is quite funny. The first place that large audiences saw the film was in a café in Paris. Amazed by the images shown on the white sheet, people lined up and waited for hours to see the ten-minute film. The Lumière brothers quickly became the men to whom the world turned its attention. The brothers sent movie photographers around the world, all of whom were told to film exotic locations, because people wanted to see moving pictures of these faraway lands. The movies that were made did not have any sound, however. Sound was added in the late 1920s.

Unit 11 Achievement Test

Chocolate is a food that is known and loved around the world. The Aztecs are the ones who first enjoyed chocolate, which they drank with chili. They shared their enthusiasm for the "drink of the gods" with Spanish explorers, whom they met in the 16th century. It is believed that Queen Isabella of Spain first tasted chocolate when she was feeling depressed. The chocolate, which has antidepressant qualities, seemed to lift her mood immediately. The chocolate that Europeans drank did not contain chili but did contain sugar, which counteracted the bitterness of the beverage. A new, profitable market for the product grew among European nobility, whose appetite for the chocolate beverage was widespread by the 17th century. Most of the chocolate that is consumed today is not drunk, but eaten, thanks to a chocolatier in England, who produced the first solid chocolate in the mid-19th century. The chocolate bars that he produced became so popular that he became the wealthiest man in England, next to the king. The chocolate you see today is made much the same way as it was then.

Unit 12 Achievement Test

There is a problem plaguing marriages today. The problem to which I'm referring is poor communication between husbands and wives. Disagreements between couples, cases of which will occur even in the best of marriages, can be resolved through effective communication skills.

Couples wishing to improve their communication are invited to the Marriage and Communication Workshop. This three-day workshop, featuring Dr. Reese Sinclair, will help you learn the skills necessary for a peaceful, loving marriage. This is the workshop that couples have been raving about. The skills presented in the workshop will change your marriage for the better. You will learn how everyone who wants to feel appreciated will respond to both verbal and nonverbal signs of acceptance. You will also learn the seven secrets of understanding the person you are talking to. In addition, you will receive invaluable books written by Dr. Sinclair that are not sold in bookstores. The ideas discussed in the books will serve as your reference long after the workshop is over. This is the opportunity you've been waiting for. Reserve your seats for the workshop, held at the Central Library, by calling now, or log on to www.centrallibrary.com.

PART IV Achievement Test

Many people working separately contributed to the invention of the telephone. The first working telephone is now credited to the Italian inventor named Antonio Meucci. He demonstrated his telephone publicly in New York in 1850, an account of which was written in an Italian language newspaper. The telephone, which used electricity to transmit sound across electric wires, was a breakthrough in communication. The most famous first telephone call, made by Alexander Graham Bell, was to his assistant, Mr. Watson. Bell, having just spilled some battery acid on himself, said "Mr. Watson, come here. I want to see you!" The telephone that they built underwent some changes, including improvements in the volume. The first telephone system that existed was organized by Bell in 1877. The circular dial with numbers, developed eleven years later, allowed people to dial different telephone numbers. Thomas Edison is another person to whom history owes some credit for the telephone. He improved the mouthpiece on the phone so that sounds were clearer, and it is the same style of mouthpiece that is still produced today. There are many other people who helped to invent the telephone, all of whom have improved our ability to communicate today.

PART V Diagnostic Test

Adoption is a legal action that is taken to create a parent-child relationship between people who are not related by blood. There are several reasons why children are put up for adoption. One is that the birth parents feel they are not prepared to care for their child. Another is that sometimes parents lose their parental rights due to abuse or neglect of their children. And, in some cases, children are left alone because their parents have died.

When a child is adopted, he or she is regarded by law as being a full member of the adopted family and is said to have all the same rights as a biological child. This means that the adopted child should be given the same love and care that a biological child is given.

Adoption laws are often found to be complex. The adoption process is complicated by the fact that it is regulated differently in each state and country. Some efforts are being made to standardize adoption laws. However, it is recommended that people wishing to adopt work with a lawyer specializing in adoption law.

The process can sometimes be long and frustrating, but with time and effort, adoptions can be completed successfully.

Unit 13 Achievement Test

When you're in a hurry, the last thing that you want to think about is safety precautions that take extra time. But the second that it takes to put on a seat belt could give you extra years of life. Just ask Doug Banhar.

Doug was asked to be at work early one morning. He was in a hurry when he left the house, but he took a second to make sure that his seat belt was fastened before he started driving. It's a good thing he did, because that second saved his life. As he was driving, an animal suddenly ran into the road. He swerved to avoid the animal, but he hit a tree. Because Doug's seat belt was on, he did not get hurt badly. Only his leg and hand were cut. He was taken to the hospital, where he was examined and released. Thanks to his seat belt, Doug was given a second chance at life. Without it, he could have been thrown from the car.

So what's your excuse for not wearing a seat belt? They're uncomfortable? Today's seat belts are made to be more comfortable than they used to be. You're a good driver? Even if you consider yourself a good driver, you may still be hit by a bad driver. You just don't want to? Wearing a seat belt is required by law. And most importantly, seat belts can save your life.

Unit 14 Achievement Test

An asteroid is defined as a rock that circles, or orbits, the sun. Asteroids and planets are related: both follow regular orbits around the sun, but asteroids are much smaller than planets. Most of the asteroids that are found in our solar system are located between Mars and Jupiter. But there are thought to be thousands more that we haven't yet discovered. Most asteroids are quite small and not considered dangerous by scientists, but there are some which are believed to be potential threats to Earth. As a result, telescopes with computers have been developed to detect asteroids that could collide with the Earth.

PART V Achievement Test

Organic farming refers to a method of farming in which no chemicals or pesticides are used to grow plants or raise animals. It is considered by some people to be an environmentally friendly way to farm. Land doesn't become polluted by chemicals when food is raised organically. Also, it is believed that people are less likely to get sick from organic food than from food that is grown conventionally.

So why are chemicals and pesticides used if they're not good for the land or for us? The main reason is that fruits and vegetables that have been treated with pesticides are less likely to be eaten by insects; therefore, production is greatly increased. This means that more food is made available at a lower cost. For this reason, the use of chemicals and pesticides is regarded by many as a way to improve standards of living, especially in developing countries.

Special caution should be taken when choosing fresh food for children, whose tolerance levels for chemicals are believed to be much lower than those of adults. The chemicals found in some foods may make children sick. It is recommended that only foods that have been grown organically be given to children until they weigh at least seventy pounds, or thirty-two kilograms. This recommendation is fairly easy to follow, as many organic products are now sold in regular grocery stores.

PART VI Diagnostic Test

Coming this week on *Survival*: Animals are able to defend themselves in some amazing ways. Animals continue to survive because they are naturally equipped to protect themselves. Humans are not. Without weapons, it probably would have been impossible for humans to have survived to this day. First, humans had sticks and stones; then they went on to develop gunpowder, then nuclear bombs. You'll be amazed to discover the awe-inspiring ways in which animals—and humans—defend themselves. You won't want to miss it, this week on *Survival*.

Unit 15 Achievement Test

Daniel Larsen, a writer for musical theater, does not avoid working hard to reach his dreams, but then for him, working with music is play. As a youth, Larsen was interested in becoming a pharmacist like his father. He recalled having been afraid to pursue his love of music because he was not sure if he would make money. However, he reconsidered following in his father's footsteps after two unhappy years of working as a pharmacist, and no time for his music. Larsen has always enjoyed writing music, so his spending long hours composing felt more like fun than work. When he finished arranging his first serious musical, "Soft Step," he found a local theater and began rehearsing it. His big break came when someone from a New York production company saw the show and proposed putting it on Broadway. Larsen's following his dreams was about to pay off, but he had some things to learn before making it big on Broadway.

Unit 16 Achievement Test

This is "Science Today," and I'm Michael Edson. There are many ways to say that something has a smell. We might use the words *fragrance* or *aroma* to talk about a good smell, or if we want to express that something smells bad, we use *stench* or *stink*. Dogs and many other animals are lucky (or perhaps not so lucky) to have a very keen sense of smell. Our noses are not nearly as sensitive, but they are good enough to smell a leaking gas pipe or food cooking in the kitchen. Our sense of smell also helps us to taste. If you have ever tried to enjoy a meal when you had a stuffy nose, you will probably remember that the food seemed to have tasted rather bland, like it needed to be seasoned. This hour on "Science Today," we are going to talk about the sense of smell. Stay with us.

PART VI Achievement Test

Today on "The Dan Webb Show," we're talking about fear. Fear is a natural emotion that most people are able to keep under control. It has made it possible for people to protect themselves from danger since the beginning of time. Some people, however, do not deal well with negative events, and they seem to allow fear to control their lives. You might be surprised to learn about the many faces of fear, so you'll want to stay tuned to the "The Dan Webb Show."

PART VII Diagnostic Test

BRIAN: Did you read the paper this morning? There's an article on the front page that says our competitors found a cure for the common cold.

STEPHANIE: I know! The news is everywhere. I heard it on the radio this morning. But I don't believe it. Clearly, it can't be true. No way can there be a cure.

BRIAN: What? Why not?

STEPHANIE: Well, although we have made some advances in understanding colds, I don't believe the news because cold viruses change all the time. Plus, there are hardly any facts in the news reports I've heard. Therefore, I need to see more proof before I believe it.

BRIAN: Well, here's the article in black and white. I think you should read it. Our company may be in trouble.

Unit 17 Achievement Test

WORLD REVIEW: Dr. Das, you mention in your book that television is one factor contributing to the breakdown of the family. Please talk about that.

DAS: Certainly. Today, we often find that both parents have to work to make ends meet. Seldom do they have enough time for all the things they want and need to do. When these parents come home from work in the evening, they are usually very tired. Unfortunately, they will use the television as a babysitter, just so they can get some chores done. However, if a television is on constantly, as it is in many homes, there are certainly fewer opportunities for the members of the family to interact and to communicate.

Unit 18 Achievement Test

WORLD REVIEW: Dr. Das, when you were here last time, we talked about how television can influence a family. Today, let's turn our attention to communication. Communication seems to be deteriorating wherever we look. Why is that?

DAS: Time is one factor. If people are so busy, they are less likely to communicate face to face.

WR: What about the role of television?

DAS: Television may also reduce communication between family members since it is often difficult to watch TV and carry on a conversation at the same time. Before television was widespread, there were more quality conversations. TV may especially influence children's development of communication skills because they don't have as much interaction with others as children did before television. Even if children watch only one hour of TV per day, they tend to have worse communication skills than children who watch no TV.

Unit 19 Achievement Test

[Introduction]

Welcome to "World View." I'm Desiree Savage. There are more people on the Earth today than ever before. This means there is also more food available, allowing people to survive on the one hand, but using more of the world's resources on the other. Because the world's population continues to rise, some scientists believe that slowing population growth is necessary.

[Second Part]

Observing that population is growing faster than our ability to produce food, some scientists believe that it is desirable to stop population growth. How would this work? Having reached childbearing age, parents would have only two children. Economists, on the other hand, argue that it is not possible for a country to have economic growth while limiting population growth. China has been the country most concerned with slowing its population growth. While discussing the problem, Chinese government officials realized that China would not be able to support the population growth much longer. Before limiting the size of Chinese families, the members of the Chinese government consulted with scientists to see what the effects would be. After realizing that the benefits would outweigh the disadvantages, the Chinese government adopted a policy of allowing only one child per family. We'll be talking about the effects of China's population policy today on "World View."

Unit 20 Achievement Test

When the car was invented, I don't think anyone could have predicted how it would change the world. It is convenient to travel by car. On the other hand, there are disadvantages to having so many cars. In fact, cars are so widespread today that traffic is terrible in many cities, including our own. For this reason, I propose that we build an underground metro. The metro should be attractive and convenient; otherwise, people will not use it. In Paris, for example, you can buy a metro pass that will take you anywhere the metro goes. However, it takes time to build an underground metro. Meanwhile, people should depend on buses. In conclusion, we need to do something about the terrible traffic in our city, and I think a metro would help solve the problem.

PART VII Achievement Test

BRAD: Did you see the letter from Aunt Helen? She's hosting a family reunion.
LINDA: I know! I saw it as soon as I got home. But I was thinking that maybe it's a mistake. No way did I ever think I would hear from her.
BRAD: What? Why not?

LINDA: Well, even though I have no problem with her, she and Mom stopped talking years ago because Helen got all Grandpa's land when he died. So, I've never even met her.
BRAD: Well, here's her number in the letter. Let's call her and find out more about the reunion.

PART VIII Diagnostic Test

Where parents send their children to school is an important decision, and experts say parents should consider all the advantages and disadvantages of both public and private schools before making a decision. However, some people don't know how public and private schools are different. This report may help.

In the United States, the issue of who pays for the schools is what differentiates public and private schools. While the government pays for public schools, organizations not associated with the government pay for private schools. Private schools also charge students tuition, which is a fee that helps pay for the costs of instruction. One disadvantage of private schools is how high tuition costs are. The fact that private schools charge tuition is one reason many children go to public schools. Since private schools are not paid for by the government, they do not have to follow certain government regulations. For example, last year many parents said that they sent their children to private schools for religious training. (The U.S. government says that this is prohibited in public schools.) Additionally, in public schools the government decides what requirements to follow for attendance and graduation, while private schools may establish some of their own requirements. How private schools use this freedom can vary considerably. Most private schools try to determine what requirements fit the needs of their students before they decide school policies.

Whether to send your child to a private or public school is a big decision. Parents must recognize that each type of school is very different. Experts claim that parents should carefully research any school they are considering to see whether or not it is right for their children.

Unit 21 Achievement Test

Many people think the first electronic digital computer was invented in Pennsylvania by John Mauchly and J. Presper Eckert. In fact, records say that the men applied for a patent for their computer in 1946. However, in 1973 a court decided that two other men, John Vincent Atanasoff and Clifford Berry, were the legal inventors of the first electronic digital computer. How could this have happened? Who were the real inventors?

It was well known that a computer was being built by Atanasoff and one of his graduate students, Clifford Berry, from 1937 to 1942. They built their computer in the basement of the physics building at Iowa State University in Ames, Iowa. What made this invention unique was its use of binary arithmetic, which is a way of representing numbers with only ones and zeros. The 700-pound machine used this system to perform 150 billion operations in 15 seconds.

John Mauchly, an engineer from Philadelphia who had corresponded with Atanasoff about his work, visited Atanasoff in 1940 while Atanasoff was building his computer. It isn't known what the men talked about or what Atanasoff showed Mauchly, but several years later Mauchly had built his own electronic digital computer in Pennsylvania!

Eventually, a court battle took place about who should collect profits from Mauchly and Eckert's computer. One organization did not want to pay Mauchly and Eckert because they knew that the same concept had been developed earlier by Atanasoff and Berry. So how did the confusion happen? What many claim is that Atanasoff began the patent process for his invention, but he had to leave the university suddenly in 1942 for government work concerning World War II. Why the university failed to complete the patent during his absence remains a mystery. While some people may not have realized the importance of Atanasoff's invention at the time, historians now state that it was the first electronic digital computer ever developed. Unfortunately, professors in the physics department at Iowa State University claim that this computer was thrown out because storage space was needed in the basement. However, a model of the original computer was completed at Iowa State University in 1997 to honor Atanasoff and Berry and their significant invention.

Unit 22 Achievement Test

The results of the 2004 presidential election in the United States caused many doubts about the accuracy of exit polls. On election night, exit polls predicted that one candidate would win, yet when the actual votes were counted, a different candidate turned out to be the winner. Because of this discrepancy, many U.S. citizens said they had

questions about how these polls worked. They asked why the polls hadn't predicted the winner correctly.

In exit polls, voters are asked questions as they leave the places where they voted. Political scientists say that these polls help them make early estimates of election results. The polls can also provide other information. Political scientists explain that exit polls measure who votes and what issues affect who they choose to vote for.

After the actual results of the 2004 U.S. presidential election were known, political scientists told people the polls had been much less accurate in this election than exit polls typically are. One analyst said that the results were less predictive in part because of an oversampling of women. He said that women had tended to vote for the Democratic candidate. Analyst John Brown says, "Oversampling is a form of systematic error, which can negatively affect the accuracy of the poll." He says the goal is to poll large numbers of randomly selected voters to avoid systematic errors.

Political scientists explain that systematic errors are different from random errors, such as people forgetting who they voted for. They also claim that better planning can reduce systematic errors and give more accurate predictions. Finally, John Brown says, "People need to remember that exit polls are only estimates of election results and that the actual winner of an election is not decided by exit polls."

PART VIII Achievement Test

That higher education is important is evident in today's society, and the majority of parents in the United States say that it is important for their children to go to college. What higher education refers to in the U.S. is any schooling beyond high school. While students used to decide whether to go to college, now the decision most students make is where to go. This is largely because students today know that many jobs require a college education, and most of the best-paying positions certainly require a degree.

The fact that higher education is valued so highly puts a lot of pressure on students and their families. For example, students' grades are very important, and students say that this is very stressful. Students and parents must also consider how much college costs. Last year, many university students in the U.S. claimed that cost was one important factor that determined where they studied after high school. In addition, what to study in college is a big decision for students to make at a relatively young age.

Parents and teachers know that standardized testing is another source of anxiety for students. In recent years, critics of standardized testing have claimed that the tests don't measure a student's ability to succeed in universities accurately. This is why universities also look at students' high school grades and extracurricular activities when considering their applications for admittance.

PART IX Diagnostic Test

ARNOLD: I'm sure I wouldn't have so many problems if I just used common sense!

DR. CARLSON: Why do you say that?

ARNOLD: Well, I'm not a young man anymore. But on vacation, I insisted on jumping off a high cliff into a lake when I knew I shouldn't have. I knew that I might hurt myself if I jumped, but I did it anyway. I mean, people die doing stuff like that if they're not careful! If I hadn't jumped, I wouldn't have hurt my back. And had I not hurt my back, I wouldn't have missed work. If I hadn't missed work, I'd be able to pay my rent. Now, if I don't pay my rent soon, I might get evicted. I just wish I had thought about the consequences before I jumped off that cliff.

DR. CARLSON: So, you feel frustrated that all these bad things have happened to you, and you wish you had used common sense in that situation.

ARNOLD: That's right.

DR. CARLSON: Yes. Had you thought about the consequences of your actions, those bad things would never have happened. Arnold, I believe you're ready to make some serious changes in your life. If so, I suggest you start by thinking before you act. Otherwise, you will continue to have problems.

Unit 23 Achievement Test

DIANA MORKEN: Welcome back to our show, "Mind and Body." My next guest is Dr. Anthony Kapp, a psychologist who has just written a new book, *Listening to Your Intuition*. Dr. Kapp, welcome.

DR. KAPP: Thank you, Diana.

MORKEN: Dr. Kapp, in your book, you talk about intuition. Tell me about that.

KAPP: Well, intuition refers to understanding or knowing something because of a feeling rather than by considering the facts. If a person has an idea about what is true or correct in a certain situation without having logical reasons for the idea, that's intuition. In other words, intuition means that you know what you should do in a given situation even if you can't explain why. I believe that if we all paid more attention to our intuitive feelings, we would do better in life.

MORKEN: Can you give us an example?

KAPP: Sure. Let's say you're looking for a job. You wish you could find something that you're really excited about. Then you are offered a position that seems perfect for you, and at first you're really excited. But a little later you get a feeling that you shouldn't take the job, even though you don't really know why. So you start to worry: If you don't take that job, will you find another one? You convince yourself that if you don't accept the job, you'll wish you had. So you take the job. Three months later, you realize that you've made a mistake. You don't enjoy your work. Of course, you wouldn't have taken the job if you had had a logical reason not to. But you didn't have a real reason. And now you think, "If only I had listened to my intuition! If I hadn't taken this job, I could be doing something that I loved right now." In that situation, you could have gotten a better job if you had paid attention to your feelings.

MORKEN: So you're saying if you had followed your intuition, you wouldn't be in this situation.

KAPP: Exactly, so pay attention to what your intuition tells you!

Unit 24 Achievement Test

GABBY: Welcome to *The Dear Gabby Show*. Today I have a letter from Frank in Ohio. He has a problem that's pretty common. Frank's letter says:

FRANK: *Dear Gabby, My brother-in-law owes my wife and me some money. He asked that we lend him $2,000 last year as a business loan. At first, I suggested that he go to a bank for the money, but he said the bank had already turned him down. So had all his friends. He had to borrow the money from someone. Otherwise, he wouldn't have been able to start his own business. So, my wife insisted on helping him out and loaning him the money, and I agreed. It's been a year now, and I've requested that he start paying us back, but he hasn't. It's a difficult situation, and I wonder what you would recommend I do.*

GABBY: Well listen, Frank, the first thing I suggest doing is talking to your brother-in-law. Show him that you want to work with him towards a solution. Tell him you are proposing that the money be paid back little by little. In fact, if I were you, I'd make up a plan for him to start paying you back, even if it's just twenty dollars per week. With such a plan, you'll start getting your money back immediately. When you talk to him, I'd recommend that you not demand anything from him. Otherwise, he might not listen to you at all. Good luck. . . . Stay with us, you're listening to *The Dear Gabby Show*.

PART IX Achievement Test

NANCY: I wouldn't be doing so badly in college if I had followed my true interests!

MICHELLE: What do you mean?

NANCY: Well, when I first got here, I took a test to see what kind of job I might be good at. The test showed that if I liked people, which I do, then I would be great as a hotel manager. I was surprised, because I had never thought about a career in management. I wanted to go into music. But lots of musicians don't make much money if they're not incredibly talented. So I thought I'd try hotel management. But I don't really like it. If I had studied music, I wouldn't have had such a hard time with my classes last year. And were I not getting such bad grades, I wouldn't have lost my scholarship. If I hadn't lost my scholarship, I wouldn't have to work. Now, if I don't work, I can't pay for tuition. I just wish I had followed my love of music!

MICHELLE: I'm sorry, Nancy. I wish I had known about this earlier. Had I known, I would have tried to help.

NANCY: Thanks.

MICHELLE: It can be hard to study something without loving it. And I know *I'd* rather be poor and happy than rich and miserable. It's never too late to change your mind, you know. Lots of people change their majors in college. Why don't you? Otherwise, you might be unhappy for the rest of your life!

Answer Key

PART I Diagnostic Test

1 | LISTENING: NEW ALBUM REVIEW

A.
1. recognize `U3`
2. carefully `U3`
3. listen `U1`
4. 'll hear `U1`
5. will make `U1`
6. will relax `U1`
7. listen `U1`
8. 'll realize `U3`
9. heavily `U3`
10. uses `U1`

B.
1. T `U1`
2. F `U1`
3. T `U2`
4. F `U2`
5. F `U1`
6. T `U2`

C. Possible answers:

Action verbs	Non-action verbs
is preparing `U3`	recognize `U3`
is flying `U3`	realize `U3`
uses `U3`	believe `U3`
has been creating `U3`	have influenced `U3`
has made `U3`	rely on `U3`
combines `U3`	focuses `U3`
began `U3`	may be `U3`
recorded `U3`	is `U3`
listen `U3`	'll hear `U3`
will make `U3`	
will relax `U3`	
started `U3`	
had taken `U3`	

2 | WHERE'S THE NEW MUSIC?

A.
1. had heard `U2`
2. used to `U2`
3. have been listening `U1`
4. haven't heard `U1`
5. was going `U2`
6. aren't playing `U1`

B. Possible answers:

Action verbs	Non-action verbs
was singing `U3`	love `U3`
'm writing `U3`	remember `U3`
aren't playing `U3`	knew `U3`
have been listening `U3`	had heard `U3`
tell `U3`	haven't heard `U3`
used to listen `U3`	enjoyed `U3`
bought `U3`	hear `U3`
was going to tell `U3`	

3 | THE PRODUCER'S RESPONSE

1. got `U2`
2. played `U2`
3. have been expecting `U3`
4. haven't receive/have not received `U1`
5. were planning `U2`
6. realized `U2`
7. hadn't come in/had not come in `U2`
8. hope/are hoping `U3`
9. thank `U3`
10. 'll continue/will continue `U1`

4 | EDITING: WORD OF MOUTH

Note: Both contracted forms and noncontracted forms are acceptable.

BEN: What ~~do~~ *are . . . listening* you ~~listen~~ to?

DEBBY: Erin Henderson. I ~~had bought~~ *bought* `U2` her album yesterday, and I ~~was listening~~ *'ve been listening* `U1` to it ever since.

BEN: She ~~is sounding~~ *sounds* `U3` great. Where ~~do~~ *did . . . hear* `U2` you ~~hear~~ about her?

DEBBY: I ~~had worked~~ *was working* `U2` when I ~~was hearing~~ *heard* `U2` a review of this album. I actually ~~would~~ *used to* `U2` have a roommate in college who ~~use to~~ *used to/would* `U2` listen to her all the time. She ~~would~~ *used to* `U2` own all her albums, and she ~~sings~~ *used to sing/would sing* `U2` *liked* `U3` along. I ~~was liking~~ her music then, but I ~~am loving~~ *love* `U3` it now! The reviewer said that she ~~was traveling~~ *had been traveling* `U2` in the Far East before she recorded this album and that her

has / had . . . improved **U2**

style ~~has~~ really ~~improve~~ because of her

doesn't sound **U3**

experiences there. Her music ~~isn't sounding~~

's . . . matured **U1**

Asian now, or anything, but she ~~had~~ just ~~matured~~
as a singer and songwriter.

Unit 1 Achievement Test

1 | LISTENING: TRAVEL AD

1. are playing **N2**   6. arrive **N9**
2. is walking **N2**   7. 'll start **N10**
3. wish **N1**   8. 'll have **N6**
4. 've booked **N3**   9. 'll have experienced **N5**
5. land **N9**   10. 've been helping **N1**

2 | AT THE TRAVEL AGENCY

1. T **N7**   4. T **N8**
2. T **N3**   5. T **N6**
3. F **N1**   6. F **N4**

3 | RIO ITINERARY

1. leave **N9**   4. 'll have seen **N11**
2. 'll have **N6**   5. sounds **N1**
3. 'll be sight-seeing **N7**

4 | EDITING: INVITATION TO A FRIEND

*Note: Both contracted forms and noncontracted
forms are acceptable.*

Dear Rob,

have   *'ve told / told* **N4**

   I ~~will have~~ some big news! I ~~tell~~ you before

've been wanting / wanted **N3**

that I ~~will want~~ to take a vacation, right? Well,
you will never believe it, but I'm going to Brazil in

'll have been working **N11**

February for Carnival! By then, I'~~ll be working~~
for almost three years without a vacation.

've been reading **N5**

I'~~ll be reading~~ some information about Carnival
and Rio on the Internet, and it sounds amazing!

'm planning / plan **N2**

I'~~ll be planning~~ to stay there for a week.

'm staying / 'll stay / 'll be staying **N8**   *'ll visit / 'll be visiting* **N6**

I ~~stay~~ in a hotel by the ocean, and I ~~visit~~ all the

'm wondering / was wondering . . . wanted **N2**

sights! I'~~ll be wondering~~ if you want to go with

've bought **N3**

me. I'~~m going to buy~~ my tickets already, but my
travel agent says there's room in the hotel and on
the plane if you want to go.

Let me know,
Chris

Unit 2 Achievement Test

1 | LISTENING: A PUBLIC PROPOSAL

A.   **B.**
1. used to sing **N4**   1. F **N5**
2. didn't know **N1**   2. F **N6**
3. wasn't going to **N7**   3. F **N4**
4. would **N7**   4. T **N7**
5. was planning **N2**   5. T **N5**

2 | TWO MAYORS, ONE WEDDING

A.

1. met **N1**
2. had decided **N5**
3. came **N5**
4. had had **N5**
5. proposed **N1**

B.

Past progressive verbs	Habitual past event verbs
1. was working **N2**	4. used to chat **N4**
2. was going to **N7**	5. would . . . bring **N4**
3. were talking **N2**	

3 | EDITING: JIM AND NANCY, TWO YEARS LATER

   Two years after they were married, Jim and

was . . . going

Nancy's marriage ~~had~~ still ~~gone~~ strong. When

had quit **N5**

telephoned last month, Jim ~~has quitted~~ his band

was finishing / had finished **N2**

and ~~has finished~~ his degree in accounting.

wasn't singing **N2**

Although Jim ~~hadn't sung~~ in the band anymore, he

brought **N1**

said, "I've always believed that music ~~was bringing~~
us together, and we still share that." Nancy also

had been working / was working **N6**

changed careers. She ~~used to work~~ as an artist

switched **N1**

when she met Jim, but she ~~has switched~~ to
teaching art at a high school shortly after they got

used to **N4**

married. She said, "I ~~would~~ think about how cool

used to / would **N4**

we were, me an artist and Jim a rock singer. I ~~did~~

were going to **N7**

dream that we ~~would~~ be famous. Soon it became

weren't making / hadn't made **N2**

obvious, however, that we just ~~haven't made~~
enough money, so we had to change careers. I

have / 've **N3**

guess we ~~had~~ both matured a little bit."

Unit 3 Achievement Test

A.
1. wasted **N1**
2. negatively **N3**
3. prefer **N2**
4. there **N5**
5. turn off **N1**

B.
1. T **N2**
2. T **N2**
3. F **N4**
4. T **N2**
5. F **N2**

2 | BENEFITS OF TV

1. a **N1**
2. c **N2**
3. b **N2**
4. d **N2**
5. c **N2**
6. a **N1**
7. a **N1**
8. d **N1**
9. c **N2**
10. d **N1**

3 | TECHNOLOGY EXHIBIT

1. 's fixing/is fixing **N1**
2. 'm having/am having **N2**
3. 's not printing/is not printing/isn't printing **N1**
4. guess **N2**
5. love **N2**

4 | EDITING: HEALTH EXHIBIT

Note: Both contracted forms and noncontracted forms are acceptable.

YUJI: Hey, Adam. You don't sound very ~~well~~ good. Are you sick?

ADAM: Yeah, I feel ~~terribly~~ terrible **N4**.

YUJI: That's too bad. ~~I'm call~~ 'm calling **N1** because ~~there're~~ there's **N5** another exhibit downtown called Advancing Healthcare Technology. It looks interesting. Do you want to go?

ADAM: I think I'd better stay home and try to sleep.

YUJI: OK. Sleep ~~good~~ well **N3**, and ~~I'm hoping~~ hope **N2** you'll feel better soon!

PART 1 Achievement Test

1 | LISTENING: NEW MOVIE REVIEW

A.
1. know **U3**
2. artistically **U3**
3. watch **U1**
4. 'll notice **U1**
5. will leave **U1**
6. will move **U1**
7. watch **U1**

B.
1. T **U1**
2. F **U1**
3. T **U2**
4. F **U2**
5. F **U1**
6. T **U2**

8. 'll understand **U3**
9. mostly **U3**
10. acts **U1**

C. Possible answers:

Action verbs	Non-action verbs
are betting **U3**	know **U3**
combines **U3**	understand **U3**
started **U3**	think **U3**
finds **U3**	was **U3**
has appeared **U3**	may be **U3**
has done **U3**	is **U3**
watch **U3**	
'll notice **U3**	
will earn **U3**	
will leave **U3**	
will move **U3**	
began **U3**	
had spent **U3**	
has changed **U3**	
have occurred **U3**	
use **U3**	
is working **U3**	

2 | WHEN'S THE MOVIE PLAYING?

A.
1. had listened **U2**
2. used to **U2**
3. liked **U3**
4. have been checking **U1**
5. was going to **U2**
6. will be showing **U1**

B.

Action verbs	Non-action verbs
rented **U3**	think **U3**
have been checking **U3**	own **U3**
will be showing **U3**	liked **U3**
see **U3**	hope **U3**
had listened **U3**	remember **U3**
haven't seen **U3**	knew **U3**
recommend **U3**	know **U3**
answer **U3**	be **U3**
will be coming **U3**	was **U3**

3 | THE RADIO STATION'S RESPONSE

1. got **U2**
2. aired **U2**
3. know **U3**
4. will be showing **U1**
5. have been waiting **U2**
6. haven't received **U2**
7. were going to hold **U2**
8. didn't arrive **U2**
9. regret **U3**
10. hope **U3**

4 | EDITING: WATCHING A MOVIE

LIZ: What ~~you are watching~~ *are you watching*?

JAMIE: *Homeless*. I ~~had bought~~ *bought* **U2** it yesterday. I ~~was wanting~~ *'ve been wanting* **U1** the DVD ever since the movie came out.

LIZ: It ~~is looking~~ *looks* **U3** great. How ~~do~~ *did ... find* **U2** you ~~find~~ out about it?

JAMIE: I ~~had driven~~ *was driving* **U2** and was listening to the radio when someone ~~do~~ *did* **U2** a review of the movie on the radio.

I actually ~~would~~ *used to* **U2** live with a girl who ~~use to~~ *used to/would* **U2** watch movies with Sean Collins all the time. She ~~would~~ *used to* **U2** own all his videos. Whenever she watched the shows, she ~~says~~ *used to say/would say* **U2** all his lines. I ~~was enjoying~~ *enjoyed* **U3** his acting then, but now ~~I'm thinking~~ *think* **U3** he's the best! The reviewer said that before Collins started work on this last movie, he ~~was staying~~ *had been staying/stayed* **U2** at home with his son for a few months and that his acting ~~has~~ *had ...* really ~~changed~~ *changed/changed* **U2** after that. These days, he ~~isn't~~ *doesn't ... look* **U3** really ~~looking~~ any different, but he ~~had~~ *has* **U1** definitely improved as an actor.

PART II Diagnostic Test

1 | LISTENING: WORK OF ART

A.
1. must have **U6**
2. 've got to **U5**
3. 're not supposed to **U5**
4. should **U5**
5. do **U4**
6. might have **U6**
7. wasn't **U4**
8. isn't it **U4**
9. couldn't have been **U6**
10. Neither have **U4**
11. did **U4**
12. don't have to **U5**
13. 'd better not **U5**

B.
1. F **U6**
2. F **U5**
3. F **U4**
4. T **U4**
5. F **U4**
6. T **U4**
7. T **U4**
8. T **U6**
9. T **U5**
10. F **U5**

2 | HOW TO APPRECIATE ART

A.
1. don't **U4**
2. 're not supposed to/must not **U5**
3. might have been **U6**
4. ought to/should **U5**
5. doesn't have to **U5**
6. ought to/should **U5**
7. must have been/might have been **U6**
8. must not/'re not supposed to **U4**
9. couldn't have been **U6**
10. so can **U4**

B.
1. is not **U5**
2. is not **U5**
3. is **U5**
4. should not **U5**
5. might not **U6**

3 | MUSEUM SUFFERS FINANCIAL CRISIS

1. is not allowed to/will not be allowed to **U5**
2. is **U4**
3. shouldn't have been passed/should not have been passed **U6**
4. was **U4**
5. didn't have to **U5**
6. may not have done **U6**
7. are supposed to **U5**
8. aren't **U4**
9. could have done **U6**
10. didn't **U4**
11. 's got to/has got to **U5**
12. may expand **U6**
13. could be **U6**

4 | EDITING: THE NEWLY RENOVATED MUSEUM

ABBY: Hi Liza. I'm calling to let you know when I'm coming. I ~~may~~ *should/ought to* be arriving on Friday morning.

LIZA: That's great, Abby! While you're here, you *must/have got to/have to/should/ought to/can* **U5** go with me to the City Art Museum. It's fantastic!

ABBY: I ~~must~~ *should/ought to* **U5** appreciate art more, but I'm not really a big art fan.

LIZA: ~~Neither~~ I, but this museum *Neither was/am* [U4]

~~really amazing~~. You like chocolate, ~~do~~ you? *really is amazing/is really amazing* [U4] *don't* [U4]

ABBY: Of course I ~~am~~. *do* [U4]

LIZA: So ~~am~~ I. Well, this museum has chocolate in *do* [U4]

every room. You ~~have~~ seen it on the news. *might have/must have* [U6]

ABBY: Oh, I think I ~~hear~~ about that. Well, okay, it *have heard/heard/did hear/might have heard* [U4]
sounds like it ought to be fun. See you soon!

Unit 4 Achievement Test

1 | LISTENING: PACKING

A.
1. have [N1]
2. Don't [N1]
3. so [N4]
4. neither [N4]
5. is [N6]
6. isn't [N6]
7. could [N1]

B.
1. F [N7]
2. F [N4]
3. T [N4]
4. T [N4]
5. T [N6]

2 | LIVING SIMPLY

A.
1. c [N1]
2. a [N5]
3. b [N6]
4. c [N4]
5. a [N1]
6. d [N5]

B.
1. doesn't think [N5]
2. wants [N4]
3. wants [N5]

3 | MOVING TIPS

1. is [N3]
2. isn't [N6]
3. is [N3]
4. does [N4]
5. will [N4]
6. can [N5]

4 | EDITING: UNPACKING

CHARLOTTE: Mom, ~~did~~ you know where the box is *do*
with all my clothes?

MRS. PARKER: It's in your bedroom, ~~is~~ it? *isn't* [N6]

CHARLOTTE: I just looked a minute ago, but I
~~don't~~ see it. *didn't* [N1]

MRS. PARKER: Check again. I think it ~~does~~. *is* [N3]

CHARLOTTE: Oh, I found it. Hey, Mom, remember
how you were going to give away your
brown dress because you thought it was ugly?
Well, it ~~is~~. I love it! *isn't* [N5]

MRS. PARKER: So you did take it out of the box! I
was wondering where it went!

Unit 5 Achievement Test

1 | LISTENING: FRIENDLY ADVICE

A.
1. must not/mustn't [N4]
2. might [N8, N1]
3. 'm not supposed to/am not supposed to [N7]
4. 're not allowed to/are not allowed to [chart]
5. ought to have [N6]

B.
1. F [N6]
2. F [N7, N2]
3. F [N4]
4. T [N8, N1]
5. F [chart]

2 | OPEN FOR BUSINESS

A.
1. was supposed to [N7]
2. had to [N3]
3. 'd better [N5]
4. could have [N5]
5. might [N1]
6. didn't have to [N9]

B.
1. doesn't think [N6]
2. was [N3]
3. should [N9]

3 | LETTER FROM THE LANDLORD

1. were not allowed/are not allowed [chart]
2. have to put/have got to put [N3]
3. are supposed to be [N7]
4. are to pay [N7]
5. must pay [N2]

4 | EDITING: WHAT I'VE LEARNED

My restaurant's been open for a couple of
months now, and things are going much better
than they were in the beginning. I really ~~have done~~ *could/should have done*
my homework better before opening my restaurant,
I ~~admitted~~! Here are two things that I have *must/have to/have got to admit* [N3, N1, N2]
learned . . .

First, I ~~have saved~~ enough to buy my own *should/ought to have saved* [N6]
building for the restaurant instead of renting. My
contract said I wasn't supposed to make many of
the changes that I thought were necessary, so I
~~have saved~~ myself a lot of trouble if I had bought *could/might have saved* [N8]
a building instead. I don't know if this could have
been possible, but I ~~have tried~~. *might/could have tried* [N8]

Second, the law says I ~~am not~~ pay my employees without taking out city taxes. A friend

didn't have to **N9**

of mine told me I ~~didn't have~~ because the restaurant is outside the city limits, but he was wrong. So, I've had to change the way I pay my workers.

That's all I will write for now. I'm sure I'll add more as my restaurant experience increases!

Unit 6 Achievement Test

1 | LISTENING: WORRIED MOM

A.
1. might have **N5**
2. must have **N4**
3. may not have been **N5**
4. couldn't . . . have **N5**
5. might not **N3**
6. should **N6**

B.
1. isn't **N2**
2. not sure **N3**
3. almost **N6**

2 | LOST CELL PHONE

A.
1. 's got to **N2**
2. might/may **N3**
3. may have **N5**
4. may not **N3**
5. might not have **N5**
6. may/might **N3**

B.
1. F **N2**
2. F **N3**
3. T **N4**
4. T **N3**
5. F **N5**

3 | MISSING WOMAN FOUND

1. might have been wearing **N3**
2. might have been upset/might be upset **N3**
3. could have been **N5**
4. may have been/may be **N5**
5. couldn't have been/could not have been **N5**
6. might not have arrived **N5**

4 | EDITING: JOURNAL ENTRY

Dad yelled at me for upsetting Mom tonight. He said she was about to call the police because I

might have been

was late. At first, I thought that she ~~is~~ overreacting because I was only a couple of hours late. But Dad told me that they had just seen a news report about a missing woman. Then I understood how

had to/must **N4**

she felt—she ~~could~~ have been worried sick! I

could **N5**

would have called, but I ~~might~~ not have imagined

should/ought to talk **N6**

that she would get so worried. I ~~talk~~ to her tomorrow and tell her how it bothers me that she

might not/may not **N3**

worries so much about me. She ~~musn't~~ understand, though. She's my Mom, so she may never stop worrying about me.

PART II Achievement Test

1 | LISTENING: THE OLD MALL

A.
1. has to have **U6**
2. Aren't you supposed to **U5**
3. ought to **U5**
4. did **U4**
5. could have **U6**
6. didn't **U4**
7. do **U4**
8. must not **U6**
9. can **U6**
10. do **U4**
11. might **U5**
12. don't have to **U5**
13. shouldn't be **U5**

B.
1. F **U6**
2. F **U5**
3. T **U5**
4. F **U5**
5. T **U5**
6. T **U4**
7. F **U6**
8. F **U4**
9. F **U4**
10. T **U5**

2 | E-MAIL TO CITY COUNCIL

A.
1. might not **U5**
2. haven't **U4**
3. couldn't have been **U6**
4. should not **U5**
5. can't have been **U6**
6. might **U5**
7. should **U5**
8. don't have to **U5**
9. had better not **U5**
10. So can **U4**

B.
1. found **U6**
2. is not **U5**
3. would **U5**
4. has not **U6**
5. can **U4**

3 | MALL SUFFERS FINANCIAL CRISIS

1. must not **U5**
2. are/have been **U4**
3. shouldn't have remained **U6**
4. didn't have to **U5**
5. might not have done/might not have been doing **U6**
6. are supposed to **U5**
7. aren't **U4**
8. could have done/could have been doing **U6**
9. didn't **U4**
10. must take **U5**
11. have to repair **U5**
12. may retile **U5**
13. might ask **U5**

4 | EDITING: MALL REOPENS

TINA: Hi Kelly. I just want to let you to know when I'm coming. I'm leaving my house

ought to/should

Saturday morning at 9:00. I ~~might~~ arrive at your house by 11:00.

must / have got to / have to / should / ought to **U5**

KELLY: Great! While you're here, you ˄go with me
to the mall. It's fantastic!

shouldn't / should not / ought not to **U5**

TINA: Well . . . I ~~am not allowed to~~ say no, but
you know that I don't enjoy shopping much.

Neither do **U4**   *is incredible* **U4**

KELLY: ~~Neither~~ I, but this mall really ~~incredible~~.

are **U4**

You're not against free food, ~~aren't~~ you?

I'm not **U4**

TINA: Of course ~~I don't~~.

am **U4**

KELLY: Neither ~~do~~ I. Well, this mall has free food
this Saturday to celebrate its reopening. You

may / might / must / could have **U6**

~~have~~ seen it in the news.

TINA: I don't watch the news much, so I probably

haven't heard / didn't hear **U4**

~~don't heard~~ about it. I am interested, though.
See you Saturday!

PART III   Diagnostic Test

1 | LISTENING: ANIMAL SHELTER ADVERTISEMENT

A.
1. a cat **U8**
2. loving new homes **U10**
3. a pet **U7**
4. greatest **U10**
5. second chance **U7**
6. Each **U9**

B.
1. F **U7**
2. T **U10**
3. T **U10**
4. T **U9**
5. T **U7**
6. T **U8**
7. F **U9**
8. T **U10**

2 | PET THERAPY

1. pet **U8**
2. a great deal of **U9**
3. a healthy choice **U8**
4. stress-related **U10**
5. stress **U7, U8**
6. music **U8**
7. animal friends **U10**
8. chance of survival **U7**
9. heart-warming **U10**
10. highly positive influence **U10**
11. conversation **U7, U8**
12. more **U9**
13. the **U8**
14. any **U9**
15. Some **U7, U9**

3 | THE GREATEST GIFT

1. b **U7**
2. b **U9**
3. d **U7**
4. c **U10**
5. a **U10**
6. c **U8**
7. d **U9**
8. a **U8**
9. b **U10**
10. c **U8**

4 | LITTLE HERO

1. small white dog **U10**
2. 42-year-old **U10**
3. a diabetic **U7**
4. house **U8**
5. The neighbor **U8**
6. a wonderful, incredible dog / an incredible, wonderful dog **U10**
7. the Netherlands **U8**
8. keen sense **U10**
9. sugar **U8**
10. the sugar level **U8, U10**
11. a second chance **U7**

5 | EDITING: THE OPERA-SINGING PARROT

talented

Polly Chord is a remarkably ~~talent~~ musician.
But so are many people, so why is Polly interesting?

37-year-old **U10**

Because Polly isn't a person—she is a ~~37 years old~~
parrot that sings ~~x~~ opera. Among her favorites
are "Quand je vous aimerai" from Bizet's *Carmen*
and "O Mio Babbino Caro" from Puccini's *Gianni*

parrots **U8**

Schicchi. It is not unusual for ~~parrot~~ to sing opera
if they hear it enough, but what is unusual is

the **U7**

˄pure joy Polly seems to get from singing it. As

U8 ,

she sings, her pupils dilate, she fluffs her green˄

, **U10**

yellow and red feathers, and she stretches her
wings ˄ and spins around as though she were

the **U8**   *a* **U7**

dancing. She displays ˄ same enthusiasm over ˄ cup
of apple sauce, her favorite food. Polly has ˄ not

any **U9**

had ~~some~~ formal musical training, but she has

A few **U9**

developed a love of singing opera on her own. ˄ ~~Few~~
of Polly's other vocal talents, though less
noteworthy, include imitating a rooster and the

a **U8**

sound of ~~the~~ doorbell.

Unit 7   Achievement Test

1 | LISTENING: FIRST DAY OF CLASS

A.
1. electricity **N3**
2. freedom **N6**
3. seats **N2**
4. assignments **N2**
5. fun **N6**

B.
1. bell (N2), topics (N2), semester (N2)
2. Dr. Smith (N1)
3. phenomena (N7b)
4. [No nouns here.]
5. energy (N3), hydrogen (N3), sugar (N3)

2 | COUNT AND NON-COUNT NOUNS

1. N (N2)   5. C (N5)
2. C (N2)   6. N (N3)
3. N (N3)   7. N (N3)
4. C (N5)   8. N (N3)

3 | NON-COUNT NOUNS IN COUNTABLE FORMS

1. flash (N4)   3. grains (N4)
2. piece (N4)   4. game (N4)

4 | EDITING: COLLEGE TALK

ED: Are you taking ~~an economics~~ this semester?
economics / an economics class

JULIE: No, I'm taking ~~a history~~ with Mr. ~~anderson~~
history / a history class (N7a) *Anderson* (N1)
instead.

ED: Oh, I took his class. I really like him, but
some ~~peoples~~ don't.
people (N8)

JULIE: I like him. Right now we're reading about
the native ~~people~~ of Australia, like the Djiki
peoples (N8)
Manunu and the Djikirritipi. The class is
really interesting, but it takes ~~times~~ to do all
time (N5)
the readings.

Unit 8 Achievement Test

1 | LISTENING: THE FUTURE OF TECHNOLOGY

A.
1. technology (N4c)
2. the greatest inventions (N6)
3. electricity (N4c)
4. the radio (N7)
5. a fax machine (N1, N4b)

B.
1. D (N3)   5. D (N6)
2. I (N1)   6. D (N5)
3. G (N7a)   7. G (N7a)
4. G (N7a)   8. I (N1)

2 | HYDROGEN CARS

1. a guy (N2)
2. a company (N1)
3. hydrogen cars (N4)
4. Dr. Tanner (N3)
5. an energy revolution (N1)

6. problems (N4a)
7. time (N3)

3 | WILDLIFE IN NATIONAL PARKS

1. the buffalo (N7b)
2. the most common mammals (N6)
3. the United States (N8c)
4. a comeback (N1)

4 | EDITING: HYDROGEN POWER FOR YACHTS

You may have heard of ~~hydrogen car~~, but have
hydrogen cars / a hydrogen car
A (N1)
you heard of a hydrogen boat? yacht manufacturer
has created a new hydrogen-powered yacht called
The (N2)
The Agua Limpia. yacht makes use of clean
energy that converts hydrogen and oxygen into t~~he~~ (N4c)
water. This technology could make t~~he~~ sailing (N4c)
possible without polluting planet's waters. It's
the (N6)
some of most exciting technology in recent news.
the (N6)

Unit 9 Achievement Test

1 | LISTENING: PAPERLESS OFFICE

A.   **B.**
1. a little (N3)   1. b (N2d)
2. Many (N3)   2. b (N2d)
3. fewer (N3)   3. a (N4)
4. any (N5)   4. b (N3)
5. most (N2d)   5. a (N4)
6. more (N3)
7. a great deal of (N2c)

2 | PAPERLESS TAX RETURNS

1. N (N3)   4. Y (N4)
2. N (N3)   5. N (N2b)
3. N (N6)   6. Y (N5)

3 | PAPERLESS CLASSROOM

1. b (N2a)   5. c (N6)
2. a (N3)   6. a (N2a)
3. c (N3)   7. b (N2c)
4. a (N2d)

4 | EDITING: SURVEY

Business Weekly conducted a survey of nearly
one thousand employees working at 200 self-
described "paperless offices" worldwide. This has
been an area of ~~few~~ research, and ~~much~~ of us here
little   *many / a lot / plenty* (N4)

at the magazine were surprised at the results. We

a great many / a lot / many / plenty **N4**

found that ~~a great deal~~ of these offices still use some paper. Only twelve percent of the employees we talked to said that they use less than one sheet

fewer **N3**

of paper at work per day. Even ~~less~~ of the people

A few / Some / Few **N3**

told us that they use no paper at all. ~~A little~~ of them work for companies where paper is prohibited. Among the employees who work in truly paperless offices, seventy percent report

a **N3**

missing paper a lot, twenty percent miss paper little, and only ten percent do not miss paper at all. These results indicate that paperless offices may not be for everyone.

Unit 10 Achievement Test

1 | LISTENING: ACKERLY MANSION

A.
1. artistic **N1**
2. colorful **N5**
3. far-reaching **N6d**
4. homemade/home-made **N6c**
5. guest **N2**
6. music **N2**

B.
1. a **N2**
2. b **N6**
3. a **N3**
4. b **N1**

2 | WASSER CASTLE

1. German heartland **N1**
2. beautiful castles **N1**
3. thirteenth-century architecture **N6**
4. early rulers **N1**
5. strategically situated **N6**
6. breathtaking view **N1**
7. beautiful forested surroundings **N4**

3 | IN OTHER WORDS . . .

1. a two-story house **N6a**
2. an award-winning product **N6b**
3. round purple Brazilian stones **N4**
4. beautifully decorated homes **N6d**
5. a blue cotton dress **N4**
6. a government-approved program **N6c**
7. a boring old French film **N4**
8. a long-lasting flavor **N6b**

4 | EDITING: POSTCARD FROM WASSER CASTLE

Dear Doug,

famous Wasser Castle

I'm writing from ~~Wasser Castle famous~~ in

amazed **N3**

Germany. I was ~~amazing~~ to learn that the castle is over 1,000 years old! This is just one of the many

N5

beautiful, historic places I've visited so far. It has

exciting **N3**   **N5**

been so ~~excited~~ for me to visit such wonderful, interesting places. I bought a great book that has

prize-winning **N6**

~~prize-winning~~ pictures of many places I've seen. I'll show you when I get home.

Aaron

PART III Achievement Test

1 | LISTENING: ADVERTISEMENT FOR A HOME-BASED BUSINESS

A.
1. industry **U7**
2. a great many **U9**
3. profitable **U10**
4. exciting new opportunity **U10**
5. the business **U8**
6. dreams **U8**

B.
1. T **U8**
2. T **U9, U10**
3. F **U7**
4. F **U7, U8, U10**
5. F **U7, U9, U10**
6. F **U8**
7. T **U8, U9**
8. T **U9**

2 | MEAT IRRADIATION

1. a process **U8**
2. most of **U9**
3. the safest way **U8**
4. food-related **U10**
5. radiation **U8**
6. two-time recipient **U10**
7. possibility **U7, U10**
8. hand-washing **U10**
9. some **U9**
10. less **U9**
11. A final criticism **U7, U10**
12. highly rigorous studies **U10**
13. few **U9**
14. the **U8**
15. criteria **U7**

3 | GENETICALLY MODIFIED FOODS

1. b **U7, U10**
2. c **U7, U9**
3. d **U10**
4. a **U8, U10**
5. d **U7**
6. b **U10**
7. d **U9**
8. a **U10**
9. c **U8, U10**
10. b **U8**

4 | FOOD PRESERVATION

1. an art U7
2. mankind U7
3. a large barrel U7
4. the United Arab Emirates U8
5. the barrel U8
6. a combination U8
7. method U7, U8
8. ancient natural U10
9. the food U8
10. a few U9
11. dangerous bacterial growth U10

5 | EDITING: ANTIDEPRESSANT DRUGS

At any given time in $\wedge$ *the* United States, about ten

million people are experiencing ~~the~~ clinical [U8]
depression. Although psychological counseling and
lifestyle changes are very effective in treating
depression, chemical and natural drugs may also

be an important part of ~~treatments~~ *treatment* [U7]. No one
antidepressant drug is considered the most
effective for everyone. Rather, the best drug for an

individual is the one with the ~~least~~ *fewest* [U8, U9] negative side
effects for him or her. Some drugs can have the

~~side unwanted effects~~ *unwanted side effects* [U10] of sleeplessness and weight

gain. There is even $\wedge$ *a* [U7] chance that some
antidepressant drugs can make depression worse.

One natural $\wedge$ [U10] alternative remedy is St. John's Wort,

which usually has a lower cost and ~~few~~ *fewer* [U9] side effects

than prescription drugs. ~~Side~~ *The side* [U8] effect most
commonly associated with St. John's Wort is dry

mouth. There is a ~~2,500 years old~~ *2,500-year-old* [U10] history of using
this herb in Europe. It is available from Nutri

without a prescription as $\wedge$ *a* [U7] tea, as an oil, or in
capsules.

PART IV Diagnostic Test

1 | LISTENING: THE FIRST MOVIE CAMERA

A.
1. of which U12
2. which U11
3. walking U12
4. shown U12
5. to whom U12
6. that U11

B.
1. T U11
2. F U12
3. T U11
4. T U11
5. F U11
6. F U12

2 | ADVANCES OF VIDEO TECHNOLOGY

1. which U11
2. when U11
3. used U12
4. that U11
5. who U11
6. which U11
7. that U11
8. whose U11
9. few of whom U11, U12
10. most of which U11, U12
11. that U11
12. — U11
13. the company was looking for U12
14. where U11
15. whom U11
16. — U12
17. called U12
18. playing U12

3 | WHAT MAKES YOU HAPPY?

A.
1. contributing U12
2. making U12
3. including U12
4. found U12
5. set U12
6. feeling U12
7. experiencing U12
8. influencing U12
9. involving U12
10. creating U12

B.
1. whose U12
2. whom U12
3. who U11
4. whose U12
5. which U11
6. who U11
7. that/which U11
8. which U11
9. where U11
10. when U11
11. which U11

4 | EDITING: WILL MOVIE THEATERS GO DIGITAL?

The technology of cinema, ~~that~~ *which* has made
many advances over the years, could be headed for
a digital future. It is likely that at least one major

film ~~whom~~ [U11] you may have seen was filmed
digitally. You probably noticed, however, that the
film did not look very good. Digital films do not
look very good when played in regular theaters,

none $\wedge$ *of* [U12] which have digital screen projectors. This is
because the digital film has to be transferred

onto film ~~what~~ *that* [U11] is used to project regular movies.

As a result, the images ~~were~~ [U12] projected onto the
screen appeared fuzzy and washed-out. The
problem is that digital projectors are extremely

expensive, ~~sold~~ *selling* [U12] for eight to ten times the price of

regular projectors. The theaters ~~where~~ *which/that* [U11] have digital projectors could show their films with higher

which (U12)

image quality. However, theaters, most of ~~whom~~ make their money from drinks and popcorn, not from ticket sales, would not directly benefit from replacing their current projectors with digital ones.

(U11)

The companies that ~~they~~ distribute the films, however, would benefit from digital distribution because it is less expensive. The films that a company distributes digitally would also arrive at the theaters faster. Only time will tell whether the

where (U11)

theaters ^ we watch movies will show their films in high-quality digital, or continue as they have done for decades.

Unit 11 Achievement Test

| 1 | LISTENING: THE HISTORY OF CHOCOLATE |

A.
1. who (N3)
2. whom (N4, N8)
3. which (N8b)
4. whose (N5, N8)
5. that (N3, N8)
6. that (N4, N8)

B.
1. a (N8b)
2. b (N4)
3. a (N6, N8)
4. b (N4, N8a)
5. a (N3, N8)
6. a (N3, N8)

| 2 | DIFFERENT KINDS OF CHOCOLATE |

1. which (N8)
2. who (N3)
3. that (N3)
4. whose (N5)
5. Ø (N4, N8a)
6. that (N4)
7. which (N8)
8. Ø (N7)
9. that (N3)

| 3 | CHOCOLATE AND YOUR HEALTH |

1. when scientists seriously began (N7)
2. that prefers (N4)
3. which the body needs (N4, N8)
4. that chocolate contains (N4, N8)
5. which do not contain (N3, N8)
6. that many have claimed/that many claim (N4, N8)

| 4 | EDITING: WHICH HAS MORE CAFFEINE, COFFEE OR CHOCOLATE? |

Q: Dear Mr. Guy Health:

which

I know that coffee, ~~that~~ I usually drink after dinner, has caffeine, but what about chocolate?

which/that (N3, N6, N8)

The other night, I was at a cafe ~~where~~ has great coffee and chocolate, and I had both. I don't usually have trouble falling asleep, but I did that night. My question is, which has more caffeine, coffee or chocolate?

A: Coffee can contain eighteen times more caffeine than a one-ounce milk chocolate bar. Caffeine is the chemical stimulant that beverages such as coffee and tea contain. It is also the chemical

(N4)

which ✗ can keep you awake. On the other hand,

which (N3)

chocolate has a lot of sugar, ~~who~~ often has a stimulating effect on the body. So if you're having trouble getting to sleep, avoid them both.

Unit 12 Achievement Test

| 1 | LISTENING: COMMUNICATION WORKSHOP |

A.
1. wishing (N6)
2. featuring (N6)
3. presented (N5)
4. to (N1)
5. discussed (N5)
6. held (N5)

B.
1. b (N1)
2. a (N3)
3. b (N1)
4. b (N6)
5. a (N5)
6. a (N1)

| 2 | TALK OF LOVE |

1. both of whom (N2)
2. none of which (N2)
3. most of which (N2)
4. neither of which (N2)
5. some of whom (N2)
6. all of whose (N2)

| 3 | BOOK REVIEW |

1. highlighting (N6)
2. published (N5)
3. sounding (N6)
4. trying (N5)
5. compiled (N5)
6. released (N5)

| 4 | EDITING: COMMUNICATION AT WORK |

Around the world, there are men and women

working/who work

~~work~~ in the same office together. Communication differences between men and women, an

of (N3)

example ^ which is illustrated in the following story, can cause problems at work. For example, a

seeking/who is seeking (N6)

female supervisor, ~~seek~~ to inform her male boss about a problem employee, may not want advice

believing/who believes (N6)

from her boss. The boss, ~~believes~~ that she wants advice, begins telling her what to do with the employee, leaving the woman feeling frustrated. In addition, some studies have found that ideas

presented/which are presented/that are presented (N5)

~~which presented~~ by women in meetings may receive little response, while a man who presents nearly the same idea a few minutes later gets all the

whose (N1)

the credit. Also, the female boss ~~which~~ communication style is more like a man's is seen as having more authority. Meanwhile, the male boss ~~which~~ we read about earlier could benefit by learning about how women's communication style may differ from his own.

Ø/whom/that **N1**

PART IV Achievement Test

A.
1. named **U12**
2. which **U11**
3. having **U12**
4. including **U12**
5. to whom **U12**
6. that **U11**

B.
1. T **U12**
2. F **U12**
3. F **U11**
4. F **U11, U12**
5. T **U11**
6. T **U11, U12**

2 | EFFICIENCY

1. who **U11**
2. when **U11**
3. used **U12**
4. that **U11**
5. who **U11**
6. which **U11**
7. that **U11**
8. whose **U11**
9. few of which **U11, U12**
10. most of which **U11, U12**
11. that **U11**
12. — **U11**
13. that you should be aware of **U12**
14. where **U11**
15. — **U11**
16. from whom **U11, U12**
17. crossing **U12**
18. filing **U12**

3 | CELL PHONES AND PROBLEMS

A.
1. created **U12**
2. debated **U12**
3. related **U12**
4. preventing **U12**
5. talking **U12**
6. attempting **U12**
7. held responsible **U12**

B.
1. whose **U11**
2. which **U12**
3. which **U11**
4. which **U12**
5. that/which **U11**
6. whose **U11**
7. that/which **U11**
8. who **U11**
9. whom **U12**
10. which **U11**
11. whose **U11**
12. where **U11**
13. that/which **U11**
14. when **U11**

4 | EDITING: THE FUTURE OF CELL PHONES

                   which
   The technology of the telephone, ~~that~~ has evolved since its invention, will most likely

that/— **U11**
continue to change. A particular advance ~~what~~ you may have heard about is speech recognition. This technology is currently available, but not in cell

none of which **U12**
phones, ~~none which~~ currently have enough memory to handle it. However, in the future, a

—/that/which **U11**
voice message ~~what~~ you leave for someone could be transformed to text and sent as an email. In

produced/that will be produced/that are produced **U12**
addition, cell phones ~~that produced~~ in the future may include automatic speech translation into other languages. However, machine translation,

requiring/which requires **U12**
~~require~~ a great deal more development, may not be available for your cell phone very soon. One change that you may soon see is a cell phone

which/that **U11**
~~where~~ has the ability to store thousands of your

               which **U12**
favorite songs. Other possibilities, some of ~~whom~~ may never happen, require surgical procedures.

U11
One group of researchers that ~~they~~ wants to take "hands free" to the limit is looking into implants that are placed in a tooth. The devices that a dentist implants surgically could both receive and

U11
send messages. Or maybe the cell phones ~~when~~ we talk on in the future will be a part of us from birth, created in our DNA. Our biggest problem may then be how to dial.

PART V Diagnostic Test

A.
1. are put up **U13**
2. lose **U13**
3. is adopted **U13**
4. is said **U13, U14**
5. means **U13**
6. be given **U13**
7. are often found **U14**
8. is complicated **U13, U14**
9. is regulated **U13**
10. are being made **U13**
11. is recommended **U14**
12. be completed **U13**

B.
1. T **U14**
2. F **U14**
3. T **U13**
4. T **U13, U14**
5. F **U13**

2 | INTERNATIONAL ADOPTION

1. b **U14**   10. b **U13**
2. c **U13**   11. c **U13, U14**
3. a **U14**   12. d **U13, U14**
4. c **U13**   13. c **U14**
5. b **U13**   14. b **U13**
6. a **U14**   15. a **U13**
7. c **U13**   16. c **U13**
8. d **U13**   17. a **U13**
9. d **U14**

3 | ADJUSTING TO A NEW FAMILY

1. are planning/plan **U13**
2. be informed/get informed **U13**
3. are often made up **U14**
4. is assumed **U13, U14**
5. to be rejected **U13**
6. is thought **U14**
7. is connected **U14**
8. be regarded **U13, U14**
9. are sometimes not prepared **U14**
10. are generally not told **U13**
11. are institutionalized/have been institutionalized **U13**
12. are often found **U13**
13. is being adopted/is adopted **U13**
14. is often judged **U13, U14**
15. be thought of **U13, U14**
16. feels **U13**
17. be overcome **U13**

4 | EDITING: AN ADOPTION STORY

Hi Mark,

How have you been? It's been a really busy
year for Jim and me. As you know, we ~~are~~ married *were/got*
last spring. We knew that we wanted to adopt a
child from abroad, so we got started on the
process right away. We filled out a lot of forms,
and had them ~~checking~~ by our attorney. We were *checked* **U13**
~~interview~~ by the adoption agency. A few months *interviewed* **U13**
later it ~~was~~ finally happened—we got ~~approve~~ by *approved* **U13**
Adoptions International. We were told that our
new son was waiting for us in Russia. There was
so much to do! We had travel plans ~~making~~ by a *made* **U13**
travel agent. We learned some phrases that had ^
~~translated~~ by a Russian friend. And of course we *been* **U13**
fixed up the house for the arrival of our new son.

We got his room ~~painting~~ and had it *painted* **U13**
~~decorating~~ especially for him. *decorated* **U13**

We want him to know that he ^ considered a *is* **U14**
very important part of our family. I'm excited for
you to meet him. I'll call you when I get a chance.

Love,
Emily

Unit 13 Achievement Test

1 | LISTENING: SEAT BELTS

A.
1. was fastened **N1, N2, N3**
2. get hurt **N9**
3. was taken **N1, N2, N3**
4. are made **N1, N2, N3**
5. be hit **N4, N6**

B.
1. T **N7**
2. F **N1, N2, N3**
3. F **N3, N6**
4. F **N1, N2, N3, N5**
5. T **N1, N2, N4, N5**

2 | FOOD SAFETY

1. can be reduced **N6**
2. are spread **N1, N2, N3**
3. be cooked **N3, N6**
4. are caused **N1, N2, N4**
5. is slowed **N1, N2, N4**
6. is refrigerated **N1, N2, N3**
7. is left **N1, N2, N3**

3 | JOB PROMOTION

1. been promoted **N2, N3**
2. was held **N1, N2, N3**
3. get frustrated/be frustrated **N4**
4. being rewarded/getting rewarded **N2, N3**
5. complained **N1**
6. done **N9**
7. manicured **N9**
8. washed **N9**
9. dry-cleaned **N9**

4 | EDITING: ROCK SLIDE

A motorist ~~injured~~ when a rock slide fell onto *was injured*
Canyon Highway late this morning. Aaron Weil
was on his way to Harrison Park where his son
~~getting marry~~. Emergency medical technicians *was getting married* **N2, N7**
arrived to find that Weil's car ~~trapped~~ under the *was trapped/had been trapped* **N1, N2, N3**
rocks, but miraculously Weil ~~was~~ survived and is *N1*
in critical but stable condition. He is being ~~hold~~ *held* **N2, N3**
overnight at a local hospital for observation.

Unit 14 Achievement Test

1 | LISTENING: ASTEROIDS, A POTENTIAL THREAT?

A.
1. are related `N1, N2, N3`
2. are found `N3`
3. are thought `N5, N6`
4. considered `N5, N6`
5. are believed `N5, N6`
6. been developed `N1`

B.
1. T `N5, N6`
2. F `N3`
3. T `N2, N3`

2 | BLACK HOLES

1. are thought to have `N5`
2. are sometimes regarded `N5`
3. are said to be `N5, N6`
4. have been found in `N5, N6`
5. are divided into `N2, N3`
6. are considered to be `N5, N6`
7. is thought that `N4, N6`

3 | THE NORTHERN LIGHTS

1. was assumed `N4, N6`
2. were believed `N5, N6`
3. were thought `N5, N6`
4. was placed/had been placed `N1`
5. were all connected/are all connected `N2`
6. are regarded `N5`
7. are made up `N2, N3`
8. is believed `N4, N6`
9. are found `N3`

4 | EDITING: LIFE ON MARS

Before the age of space exploration, Mars ^was considered to be a possible home for intelligent

life. Stories about life on Mars have long ^been made up to scare and entertain us. Although Martians are

no longer thought ^to exist, it ~~believes~~ is believed that the planet supported some forms of life millions of years ago.

Fossils that ~~find~~ were found in a meteorite on Mars are

regarded ~~to be~~ as strong evidence that bacteria may have inhabited the planet at one time.

PART V Achievement Test

1 | LISTENING: ORGANIC FARMING

A.
1. is considered `U14`
2. become polluted `U13`
3. is believed `U14`
4. get sick `U13`
5. have been treated `U13`
6. means `U13`
7. is made `U13, U14`
8. is regarded `U14`
9. should be taken `U13`
10. found in `U14`
11. have been grown `U13`
12. are now sold `U13`

B.
1. T `U13`
2. F `U13`
3. T `U13`
4. T `U13, U14`
5. T `U14`

2 | VEGETARIANISM

1. b `U13, U14`
2. c `U14`
3. a `U13`
4. a `U13`
5. c `U13`
6. d `U13`
7. d `U13`
8. b `U13`
9. a `U14`
10. c `U13`
11. c `U13`
12. b `U13`
13. a `U14`
14. c `U13`
15. b `U14`
16. d `U13`
17. d `U13`

3 | RECYCLING AND REUSING

1. are located `U14`
2. be recycled `U13`
3. are picked up `U13`
4. are used `U13`
5. are probably surrounded `U14`
6. are made up `U14`
7. being destroyed `U13`
8. be reused `U13`
9. are found / can be found `U14`
10. belonged `U13`
11. are collected `U13`
12. are cut up `U13`
13. is thought `U14`
14. are believed `U14`
15. is considered `U14`
16. is often said `U14`
17. is regarded `U14`

Rosa and I bought our first house today! We offered the sellers a fair price, and our

was
offer ^accepted! It's an older home, and there are

be done U13
a lot of repairs that need to ~~do~~. I guess the house

was/is/would be U14   *afford* U13
^considered a "fixer upper." We can't ~~be afforded~~

made U13
to have all of the repairs ~~make~~ right now, but we want to start on a few projects. First I want to get

fixed U13
the roof ~~fix~~. It leaks when it rains, so of course I

repaired U13
need to have the ceiling ~~repair~~ as well. Then I'll

replaced U13
have the plumbing ~~replace~~. After those big things

cleaned U13
are done, we can have the carpets ~~clean~~ and get

painted U13
the walls ~~paint~~ and we can move in. We can hardly wait!

PART VI Diagnostic Test

1 | LISTENING

A.
1. to survive U16
2. to have survived U16
3. to develop U16
4. to discover U16
5. to miss U16

B.
1. T U15, U16
2. F U15, U16

C.
1. SC U16
2. S U16
3. O U16

2 | ANIMAL DEFENSE

1. c U15
2. c U15
3. a U15
4. d U15
5. c U16
6. d U16
7. a U16
8. b U15
9. b U15

3 | HUMAN DEFENSE

1. surviving U15
2. wearing U15
3. making U15
4. to injure U15
5. to threaten U16
6. Inventing U15
7. Having U15
8. building U15
9. developing U15
10. to improve U16
11. to employ U16
12. to use U16
13. hurting U15
14. to produce U15
15. to destroy U15
16. using U15

4 | MARTIAL ARTS

1. seems to have increased steadily U16
2. Having learned a martial art U15
3. too old to benefit U16
4. Deciding on which of the many kinds U15
5. your learning a martial art U15
6. try scaring people/try to scare people U15
7. by convincing them U15
8. a person to defend himself or herself U16
9. avoid spending time in places U15
10. feel like learning U15
11. recommend attending U15
12. Without seeing a class U15
13. be able to figure out U16
14. advise using U15
15. to attack or block U16
16. to earn/earning different belts U15, U16

5 | EDITING: DEFENDING YOUR HOME AGAINST TERMITES

to be
Your home is likely ~~being~~ your greatest

Protecting U15, U16
financial investment. ~~Protect~~ your home from

feeding U15
termites is often a great concern. Termites ~~feed~~ on the wood in your home will eventually cause great damage, so you should find a pest control company if you suspect your home has them. It is

to make U16
important ~~making~~ sure that the company is reputable. Take your time to ~~carefully~~ select a

carefully U16   *to rush* U16
good company ^. You do not need ~~rushing~~ into finding a company since termites work slowly. After you make an appointment, someone will

thoroughly U16
come to ~~thoroughly~~ inspect your home ^for termites. When the termite inspector arrives, he or

to check/checking U15, U16
she will begin ~~check~~ inside your house as well as

U15
outdoors. If termites are found ✗ eating the wood in your house, the inspector will spray the wood

Having U15
to kill the termites. ~~Have~~ been regularly treated for termites, your home will increase in value.

Unit 15 Achievement Test

1 | LISTENING

A.
1. becoming N3
2. having been N5
3. following N2
4. writing N2
5. spending N4
6. arranging N2
7. rehearsing N2, N4
8. putting N2

B.
1. a [N4]   2. b [N3]

2 | IMPROVING THE SHOW

1. C [N1]   4. O [N1]
2. C [N1]   5. C [N1]
3. S [N1]

3 | OPENING NIGHT

1. rehearsing [N3]   6. worrying [N4]
2. Having [N5]   7. Having [N5]
3. having [N3]   8. jumping [N2]
4. opening [N4]   9. coming [N3]
5. wondering [N2]   10. applauding [N2]

4 | EDITING: THE SHOW'S A HIT!

My show has been on Broadway for a month now! I'm thrilled, but I'm so tired that I feel like
sleeping
~~to sleep~~ for a week! *Having* [N5] ~~Have~~ worked so hard for so long, I can't believe I'm finally a success. I never
having [N2]
thought this would happen to me! I enjoy ~~to have~~ the opportunity to work with such talented people. Fortunately, people are recognizing my name, but
being [N2]
not my face, so I don't need to avoid ~~to be~~ in crowds yet. A Hollywood studio and I are even
adapting [N2]
discussing ~~adapt~~ the show for the big screen! I
helping [N2]
really appreciate their ~~help~~ me to follow my dreams.

Unit 16 Achievement Test

1 | LISTENING

A.   **B.**
1. to talk [N2]   1. C [N1]
2. to express [N5]   2. O [N1]
3. to have [N3]
4. to smell [N6]
5. to taste [N2]
6. to enjoy [N5]
7. to have tasted [N7]
8. to be seasoned [N7]

2 | A PLACE TO REMEMBER

1. c [N4]   4. d [N7]
2. b [N1]   5. c [N5]
3. d [N3]

3 | THE SMELL OF MONEY

1. to increase [N2]   6. to resist [N5]
2. to lure [N5]   7. to be downplayed [N7]
3. to attract [N2]   8. to have been [N7]
4. to buy [N2]   9. to have increased [N7]
5. to spend [N3]   10. to avoid [N6]

4 | EDITING: THE ARTIFICIAL NOSE

to develop
Scientists have been working ~~developing~~ an artificial nose. Their nose is designed to
detect accurately [N8]
~~accurately detect~~ toxic chemicals that should not
to build [N5]
be allowed ~~building~~ up in enclosed spaces. Many
to find [N5]
industries have been trying ~~finding~~ a way to
identify quickly [N8]
~~quickly identify~~ harmful substances. The scientists
to improve / improving [N5]
are continuing ~~improve~~ the artificial nose before making it commercially available.

PART VI Achievement Test

1 | LISTENING

A.   **B.**
1. to protect [U16]   1. SC [U16]
2. to allow [U16]   2. S [U16]
3. to control [U16]   3. O [U16]
4. to learn [U16]
5. to stay [U16]

C.
1. F [U15, U16]
2. T [U15, U16]

2 | HORROR FILMS

1. c [U15]   6. d [U16]
2. d [U16]   7. a [U16]
3. b [U15]   8. c [U15]
4. d [U15]   9. d [U15]
5. b [U16]

3 | CHILDREN AND FEAR

1. believing [U15]
2. playing/To play [U15, U16]
3. to help [U16]
4. to be [U16]
5. overdoing/to overdo [U15, U16]
6. helping/to help [U15, U16]
7. explaining [U15]
8. socializing [U15]
9. teaching [U15]
10. to hit [U16]

11. to monitor U16
12. to teach U16
13. growing U15
14. dealing U15
15. coping U15
16. to practice U16

4 | OVERCOMING SHYNESS

1. nervous to speak/nervous speaking U15, U16
2. Overcoming shyness/To overcome shyness U15, U16
3. Learning certain skills/To learn certain skills U15, U16
4. too difficult to master U16
5. Your beginning a conversation U15
6. consistently focus on helping U15
7. by talking to them U15
8. Your making a commitment to overcome U15
9. dread being in social situations U15
10. try preparing/try to prepare U15, U16
11. dare to go to a party U16, U15
12. without thinking ahead of time U15
13. able to find the courage U16
14. recommend being aware of U15
15. Sitting up straight U15
16. good skills to practice U16

5 | EDITING: HALLOWEEN CANDY

Halloween is a holiday celebrated in much of

Dressing
the western world. ~~Dress~~ in costumes and going door to door to ask for candy is a special event

marketing U15
for many children. Stores' ~~market~~ of candy has helped shape what Halloween is today, and surely

to U16
children are happy ‸receive the candy. Some children like to ~~strategically~~ choose a neighborhood

strategically U16   *to walk* U16
‸where they do not need ~~walking~~ very far between houses. Parents need to ~~thoroughly~~ check all the

thoroughly U16
candy ‸to make sure that it is safe; some might

taking U15
even end up ~~to take~~ a piece of their favorite candy, as it is very tempting! Some parents encourage their children to eat the candy as quickly as

U15
possible so that their teeth will not decay from ✗ being in contact with sugar for a long period of

brushing/to brush U15, U16
time. However, ~~brush~~ teeth immediately after eating candy is probably better for children's

eating U15
dental heath than ~~eat~~ it all at once.

PART VII Diagnostic Test

1 | LISTENING

A.
1. Clearly U17
2. No way U17
3. although U18
4. because U18
5. hardly U17
6. Therefore U20
7. here's U17

B.
1. D U18
2. D U18
3. I U18

2 | COLD MYTHS

1. Actually U17
2. just U17
3. Despite the fact that U18
4. Rather U20
5. when U18, U20
6. only U17
7. upon U19
8. because U18, U19
9. home U17
10. where U18
11. Second U20
12. suffering U17, U19
13. because U18, U19
14. Nevertheless U20
15. even if U18
16. Third U20
17. in no way U17
18. Furthermore U20
19. To summarize U20
20. catching U17, U19

3 | COLD PREVENTION

1. However, U20
2. provided you take U18
3. After studying how colds spread U19
4. Obviously, U17
5. Since this is not always possible U18, U20
6. especially if someone else in the home U17, U20
7. In addition U20
8. before thoroughly washing U17, U19
9. as U19, U20
10. even one virus U17
11. can never be too cautious U17
12. As soon as you feel U18
13. Although the medicine will not end U18
14. For example, U20
15. after blowing your nose U19

16. Given that medicine can keep **U19**
17. To conclude **U20**
18. are everywhere **U18**
19. but **U20**
20. in the meantime **U20**

4 | EDITING: UNANSWERED QUESTIONS

There are still many unanswered questions

For example
regarding the cold virus. ~~For an example~~, where

Even **U17**
do they come from? ~~Even if~~ virologists, people
who study viruses, have a poor understanding of

Changing **U19**
their origin. ~~Changed~~ over time, cold viruses are

not easily **U17**   *Given* **U19**   *never* **U19**
~~easily not~~ studied. ~~Giving~~ that viruses have ~~ever~~

changing **U17**
been observed while ~~changed~~, scientists barely

For these / Because of these **U20**
understand the process. ~~Because these~~ reasons, it is
difficult to find a cure, but many scientists are
hopeful that a cure is still possible. Said one

as **U20**
scientist, "As long ~~that~~ we continue to study

But / so / yet **U17**
colds, we will learn new things. ~~Nor~~ we should

Otherwise **U20**
never give up trying to find a cure. ~~Unless~~, we
never will."

Unit 17 Achievement Test

1 | LISTENING

A.
1. Seldom **N5**
2. home **N7**
3. in the evening **N7**
4. very **N4**

B.
1. Fre **N2**
2. S **N3**
3. Foc **N4**
4. Fre **N2**
5. S **N3**

2 | SHOULD PARENTS WORK LESS?

S
WORLD REVIEW: Obviously, parents should spend
   more time with their children, but this isn't
   easy to do, is it?
DAS: No, it isn't. Because parents work a lot,

N **N5**
rarely do they have the energy to play with

F **N4**
their children or to read to them. Parents just
need to be able to say to their children,
"Tonight, we're not watching any TV."

F **N4**
WR: You mention that parents are simply too tired
to spend time with their children after work.
Should parents work fewer hours?

S **N3**
DAS: Certainly, parents need to work to be able to

S **N3**
provide for their families, but obviously,
parents need to spend time with their children

F **N4**
as well, and not just provide food, clothing,
and shelter. If parents can manage to work

F **N4**   *N* **N5**
only part time, not only will they be less

S **N3**
stressed, but their children will clearly benefit
as well. But, in many cases, working part time

N **N5**
isn't even an option for parents.

3 | MORE EXPERT ADVICE

1. just/only **N4**
2. simply **N4**
3. even **N4**
4. Sadly **N3**
5. Rarely/Seldom **N5**
6. Seldom/Rarely **N5**
7. certainly/simply/just **N3**

4 | EDITING: PARENTS' REACTION TO THE EXPERT

usually has
SPIRO: *World Review* ~~has usually~~ great guests, but
   I don't know about today's guest.

do **N5**
ROULA: Well, I think Dr. Das is right—rarely ^ we
   get a chance to spend enough time with ^ our

can we **N6**
kids. But no way ~~we can~~ work part time!

have I **N5**
Never ~~I have~~ heard such an unrealistic idea!

is someone **N6**
SPIRO: There ~~someone is~~ out of touch with reality!

Unit 18 Achievement Test

1 | LISTENING

A.
1. wherever **N4**
2. If **N6**
3. since **N5**
4. Before **N3**
5. because **N5**
6. as **N7**
7. Even if **N6**

B.
DAS: Television may also reduce communication

1. **N1**
between family members since it is often
difficult to watch TV and carry on a
conversation at the same time. Before
television was widespread, there were more
quality conversations. TV may especially

2. **N1**

influence children's development of
3. N1

communication skills because they don't have as much interaction with others as children did before television. Even if children watch only one hour of TV per day, they tend to have worse communication skills than children that watch no TV.

4. N1

C.
1. P N4   3.   C N6
2. R N5   4.   C N6

2 | IMPROVING A COMPANY

1. Profitability will be high as long as demand is high./As long as demand is high, profitability will be high. N6

2. Many people support less packaging because excess packaging is seen as wasteful./Because excess packaging is seen as wasteful, many people support less packaging. N5

3. Others support less packaging although they recognize that the packaging helps protect the product./Although others recognize that the packaging helps protect the product, they support less packaging. N7

4. Unless teenagers are targeted by marketing specifically, they are not likely to buy our products./Teenagers are not likely to buy our products unless they are targeted by marketing specifically. N6

5. Now that gas is more expensive, the price of the products needs to be increased to pay for distribution./The price of the products needs to be increased to pay for distribution now that gas is more expensive. N5

6. Second purchases have increased whereas the number of first-time buyers has decreased./Whereas the number of first-time buyers has decreased, second purchases have increased. N7

7. Customers will be sent a "frequent buyer" promotional advertisement if they buy our products three times or more./If customers buy our products three times or more, they will be sent a "frequent buyer" promotional advertisement. N6

8. Even though the latest product is not that popular, some people love it./The latest product is not that popular even though some people love it. N7

9. The recognition of the products should remain constant while research and development continues to try to improve the products./While research and development continues to

try to improve the products, the recognition of the products should remain constant. N3

10. Most of the company's advertising is done on television despite the fact that radio advertising could be cost effective./Despite the fact that radio advertising could be cost effective, most of the company's advertising is done on television. N7

3 | EDITING: WHERE SHOULD WE OPEN OUR NEW BUSINESS?

BRADLEY: Jennifer, I've got two possible locations for our new business. One is nearby, not too far from a school, and it is located on a quiet road. The other is in the mall downtown. Which one do you think we should take?

JENNIFER: Well, ~~although~~ *if* we take the location that is nearby, we won't have to spend a lot of time driving to work. Driving to the mall daily

because/since N5

would take about an hour of our time ~~whereas~~ it is about 15 miles away on a busy road.

BRADLEY: True, but we would probably have more customers at the mall. You know, so many people go to the mall for different reasons.

Once/When N3

~~Although~~ they see our store, they might just stop in.

JENNIFER: That's possible, but remember, we are

After/Once/If N6

selling children's clothes. ~~While~~ we let parents know about our business, I think a school location might work out great!

before N3

BRADLEY: Well, ~~since~~ we decide for sure, let's visit

Even though/Although N1

both locations. ~~After~~ it will take some time, I think seeing both places will help us in our decision.

Unit 19 Achievement Test

1 | LISTENING: POPULATION GROWTH

1. using N5   2. Because N6

2 | POPULATION GROWTH IN CHINA

A.
1. While discussing the problem N2, N3
2. Before limiting the size of Chinese families N3
3. After realizing that the benefits would outweigh the disadvantages N3

B.
1. Observing that population is growing faster than our ability to produce food N5
2. Having reached childbearing age N4

3 | NEWS SHORTS

1. No **N5**
2. Yes **N7**
3. Yes **N5**
4. No **N6**
5. Yes **N3**
6. No **N3**
7. No **N4**
8. Yes **N2**
9. Yes **N3**

4 | WORLD ISSUES

1. Concerned with overpopulation, some people want to limit the size of their family. **N6**
2. Having grown slowly between the years 500 and 1700, the world's population growth then began to accelerate. **N4**
3. More and more land is cleared for farms every year, destroying animal habits. **N5**
4. While attending the conference on nuclear waste, world leaders agreed to invest money into disposing the waste safely. **N2**
5. After visiting the military base, United Nations arms inspectors reported their findings to the council./United Nations arms inspectors reported their findings to the council after visiting the military base. **N2**
6. Wanting more than two children, many parents oppose zero population growth. **N5**
7. Before hosting a conference on environmental concerns, the president first met with his task force./The president first met with his task force before hosting a conference on environmental concerns. **N3**

5 | EDITING: SUMMARY

Observing
~~To observe~~ that population and food supply grow at different rates, Malthus warned us of a
Writing **N5**
problem. ~~Wrote~~ in an essay, Malthus claimed that the world's population would grow faster than our
carried **N7**
ability to produce food. If ~~carrying~~ out correctly, the adoption of zero population growth would
passing **N3**
cause the population to stabilize. Before ~~pass~~ a law to limit population growth, Chinese government officials discussed the advantages
Having established **N4**
and disadvantages with many experts. ~~Established~~ a policy of limiting births, Chinese government officials had to enforce it. Although they have
adopting **N3**
largely been successful, since ~~having adopted~~ the
has slowed **N4**
policy, China's population growth ~~slowing~~, but nevertheless continues to rise.

Unit 20 Achievement Test

1 | LISTENING

A.
1. On the other hand **N4c**
2. In fact **N4a**
3. and **N2**
4. for example **N5b**
5. However **N3**
6. In conclusion **N5d**

B.
1. a **N4d**
2. d **N4b**
3. c **N4e**

2 | TRAFFIC AND STRESS

1. However **N4c**
2. Along with **N4a**
3. First **N5a**
4. and **N2**
5. as a result **N4d**
6. For instance **N5b**
7. otherwise **N4b**

3 | DRIVING TEST

1. Mr. Matos, you passed the exam because of your expert road knowledge. However, you could use some practice in parallel parking. **N4c**
2. Bob, when you parked uphill, you didn't turn your wheels away from the curb. Otherwise, you would have passed. **N3**
3. Jan, you didn't use a signal when you turned left at the intersection. Likewise, you didn't signal when you turned into the parking lot. **N4a**
4. Mrs. Thomas, you scraped the curb when you parked; on account of this, you lost some points. **N4d**
5. Bernie, you didn't notice the car behind you trying to pass you. Meanwhile, you were changing lanes. **N4e**
6. Alison, when the ambulance was approaching, first you should have signaled to pull over; then you should have slowed down. **N4e**
7. Ms. Adams, on the last part of the test you parked perfectly. All in all, you did very well. **N5c**
8. Alex, you lost some points by stopping too close behind the other car. You did everything else correctly, though. **N4c**
9. Stephanie, signaling before you change lanes is very important, especially when a car is behind you. **N3**

4 | EDITING: NEIGHBORS ON THE GO

Before
~~After~~ everyone had cars, people knew their
because **N4d**
neighbors ~~so~~ they would walk past each other when they came or went. Today, most people are

As a result / As a consequence / Consequently / Therefore / For this reason / Because of this **N4d**
isolated in their own cars. ~~On the contrary,~~ we have less social interaction with our neighbors.

importantly **N5a**
Most ~~important,~~ we have become less

In summary / All in all **N5c**
understanding of one another. ~~Meanwhile,~~ cars

To conclude **N5d**
have weakened our neighborhoods. ~~In addition,~~ I would like to invite you to go for a walk around your neighborhood once in a while, and if you see a neighbor, stop and introduce yourself.

PART VII Achievement Test

1 | LISTENING

A.
1. maybe **U17**
2. No way **U17**
3. even though **U18**
4. because **U18**
5. So **U20**
6. never **U17**
7. here's **U17**

B.
1. D **U18**
2. D **U18**
3. I **U18**

2 | FAMILY REUNIONS: THE BEST TIMES OF MY LIFE

1. Fortunately **U17**
2. only **U17**
3. Although **U18**
4. As a matter of fact **U20**
5. when **U18, U20**
6. Upon **U19**
7. wherever **U18**
8. only **U17**
9. since **U18, U19**
10. work **U17**
11. Second **U20**
12. playing **U19**
13. as **U19**
14. However **U20**
15. even if **U18**
16. Third **U20**
17. in no way **U17**
18. Incidentally **U17**
19. coming **U19**
20. Anyway **U20**

3 | PLANNING A FAMILY REUNION

1. After studying **U19**
2. Interestingly **U17**
3. actually be quite difficult **U17, U20**
4. Because planning a reunion **U18**
5. having even a little help **U17**
6. Even if you are not close **U18, U20**
7. by phone or by e-mail **U17**
8. Additionally **U20**
9. before requesting help **U19**
10. because your assistants will want **U18, U20**
11. can never be too prepared **U17**
12. As soon as family arrives **U18, U20**
13. For example **U20**
14. even if you have asked **U18, U20**
15. after lighting the barbecue **U19**
16. Given that people can be unpredictable **U19**

17. To conclude **U20**
18. families everywhere **U18**
19. but there can be a lot of work **U20**
20. Afterwards, however **U17, U20**

4 | EDITING: REUNION ACTIVITIES

There are many activities you can do to help

For instance
make your family reunion a success. ~~From instance,~~ you can tell stories, have a family talent show,

even **U17**
talk about family history, or ~~even if~~ make a time

not **U17**
capsule. Such activities are ~~neither~~ only fun, but they encourage everyone to interact closely, and to

As a **U20**
get to know each other better. ~~In~~ result, everyone will feel more comfortable, especially if they

Varying **U19**
haven't seen each other for a long time. ~~Varied~~ the type of activities, from sports to crafts to guessing games, you'll ensure that everyone can get

involved **U17, U19**   Giving **U19**
~~involving.~~ ~~Being giving~~ everyone a choice of activities to do at any one time can also help.

U19
While ~~being~~ planning the activities, it is a good idea to send a questionnaire to everyone you are inviting to see what they are interested in doing. Be sure to include a self-addressed, stamped

Otherwise **U20**
envelope. ~~Unless,~~ you may not get as many responses

as **U18**
~~that~~ you would like. For more family reunion

U17
activity ideas, click ~~to~~ here.

PART VIII Diagnostic Test

1 | LISTENING: PRIVATE VERSUS PUBLIC SCHOOLS

A.
1. say parents should consider **U22**
2. how public and private schools are **U21**
3. who pays for the schools **U21**
4. how high tuition costs are **U21**
5. said that they sent **U22**
6. says that this is prohibited **U22**
7. How private schools use **U21**
8. try to determine what requirements fit **U22**
9. claim that parents should **U22**
10. whether or not it is **U21**

B.

<u>Noun clause as a subject</u>
The fact that private schools charge tuition
Whether to send your child to a private or public
school U21

<u>Noun clause as an object</u>
what requirements to follow for attendance and
graduation
that each type of school is very different U21

2 | READING: CHALLENGING STUDENTS TO LEARN

1. C U22   5. C U22
2. I U22   6. I U22
3. I U22   7. C U22
4. I U22   8. I U21

3 | TALKING ABOUT SCHOOLS

1. (that) I had gone U22
2. what I think/thought U22
3. (that) the student diversity is always U22
4. (that) students come U22
5. that I had enjoyed U22
6. what that would be like U21
7. if/whether (or not) she went U22
8. (that) she did U22
9. (that) she liked U22
10. how small it was U21
11. how shy she was U21
12. how many students were U21
13. (that) there were U22
14. if/whether (or not) she (really) liked U22
15. (that) she loved it U22
16. what is/was better U21

4 | APPLYING TO A PRIVATE SCHOOL

1. (that) Winslow Academy was the best private school U22
2. what some advantages (of the school) were/are U22
3. what people always say is the best thing about U21
4. how Winslow Academy's small classes could make U22
5. (that) smaller class sizes allowed/allow U22
6. how students are chosen U22
7. (that) they always have U22
8. what he/Mr. Short meant U21
9. Mrs. Ryan/her (that) it allows U22
10. if/whether (or not) Winslow Academy had accepted U22
11. (that) how many students they accept U21

12. if/whether (or not) he/Mr. Short could interview U22
13. when he/Mrs. Ryan's son could come in U21

5 | EDITING: A LETTER HOME

Dear Mom and Dad,
      I just wanted to tell ^*you* that my new school is
great! I didn't know how much ~~would it~~ *it would* U21
challenge me to do my best. My math teacher
asked me ~~do I want~~ *if/whether (or not) I want/wanted* U21 to participate in a math
competition next month. Of course I ~~said her~~ *told her/said* U22 that
I did! ~~It~~ *That it* U21 will be a lot of fun is obvious. I need to
get ready for the competition, but I don't know
what ~~should I~~ *I should* U21 study. My new friend Sarah is going
too, so I asked her ~~did she know~~ *if/whether (or not) she knew* U21 how to prepare.
She ~~told~~ *told me/said* U22 that she didn't know either, so we are
going to ask the teacher what ⨉ *U21* we need to know.
      One thing I don't like about the new school is
that ⨉ *U21* I have to wear a uniform. What we wear
~~are~~ *is* U21 very stylish, but I ~~tell~~ *tell you/say* U22 that it is boring to wear
the same thing every day. Oh well, I'm sure I'll get
used to it. I'm off to go study.

Love,
Mariela

Unit 21 Achievement Test

1 | LISTENING: WHO *REALLY* INVENTED THE COMPUTER?

A.
1. that the men applied N1
2. that a computer was being built N1
3. What made this invention unique N1
4. what the men talked about N4
5. that the same concept N1
6. that it was the first N1
7. that this computer was thrown out N1

B.
1. T N2
2. F N4
3. T N4

C.

Noun clause as a subject
What many claim
Why the university failed to complete the patent during his absence **N1**

Noun clause as an object
that two other men, John Vincent Atanasoff and Clifford Berry, were the legal inventors of the first electronic digital computer
what Atanasoff showed Mauchly **N1**

2	AN INTERVIEW WITH JOHN MAUCHLY

1. I'm not sure how my computer is different (from Atanasoff's computer). **N4**
2. I don't know how Atanasoff's computer works. **N4**
3. It's difficult to say whose computer is better. **N1**
4. I don't know when I will finish building my computer. **N4**
5. It is questionable if/whether (or not) Atansaoff knows that I am building a computer too. **N7**
6. It's difficult to say what my computer looks like. **N5**
7. I don't know if/whether (or not) Atanasoff has a patent for his computer. **N1**

3	A SUBSTITUTE TEACHER

1. I want to ask (Jim) who missed class. **N5**
2. I want to ask (Jim) if he collected the homework from yesterday. **N6**
3. I wonder how long the students took to complete the reading activity. **N4**
4. I wonder what the class talked about during discussion time. **N4**
5. I wonder what he told the students to do for homework. **N4**
6. I want to ask (Jim) where he put the key to my classroom. **N4**
7. I want to ask (Jim) whether or not he had fun teaching my class. **N7**

4	EDITING: HOW DID THE PATENT APPLICATION GET LOST?

May 14, 1942

Dear Professor Costel:
    What I left on your desk is a file that Professor Atanasoff gave me. You probably know
that
~~the fact that~~ he left today for the East Coast. But
left **N5**
did you know that he ~~did leave~~ a lot of equipment
That the **N2**
in the basement? ~~The~~ equipment is crowding the basement is obvious. Please advise on what

I should **N4**   *if/whether (or not)* **N6**
~~should I~~ do with it. I don't know I should throw it out. Also, please note that he left some papers for you to sign. He said that they should go over to Beardshear Hall after you have signed them so the patent application can be filed. I'll see you when I return from vacation.

Best,
Joyce

Unit 22 Achievement Test

1	LISTENING: EXIT POLLS

A.
1. asked why the polls hadn't predicted **N4**
2. say that these polls help **N2**
3. explain that exit polls measure **N2**
4. told people the polls had been **N2**
5. said that women had tended **N1**
6. says the goal is **N1**
7. claim that better planning can **N1**

B.

Indirect speech
many U.S. citizens said they had questions about how these polls worked
One analyst said that the results were less predictive in part because of an oversampling of women. **N1**

Political scientists explain that systematic errors are different from random errors, such as people forgetting who they voted for. **N1**

Direct speech
Analyst John Brown says, "Oversampling is a form of systematic error, which can negatively affect the accuracy of the poll."
Finally, John Brown says, "People need to remember that exit polls are only estimates of election results and that the actual winner of an election is not decided by exit polls." **N1**

2	AN EXIT POLL INTERVIEW

1. if he was completely satisfied **N3**
2. what the most important issue was **N4**
3. (that) funding for higher education was the most important issue **N1**
4. (that) environmental policies could affect **N7** /(that) environmental policies were another issue that could affect **N7**
5. whether or not he would vote in the next election **N3**

3 | A POLITICAL SCIENCE CLASS

A.
1. would `N7`
2. vote `N6`
3. might `N7`
4. thought `N5`
5. could `N7`
6. if/whether (or not) `N3`

B.
1 I `N3`
2 C `N4`
3 I `N4`

4 | EDITING: A LETTER TO PROFESSOR POLITICS

Dear Professor Politics,

I am very upset at how deceiving the early exit polls were during last week's election. When I went to bed on election night, the newscaster ~~told~~ *said* that Matthew Long had the most votes. When I woke up, my husband asked who I ~~think~~ *thought* `N5` had won the election. Of course, I told him that ~~yesterday~~ *the day before / the previous day* `N8` the polls had said Long would win. Then he told me the newspaper had reported Ron Black as the winner, not Long! At first I didn't believe him, so he said I could read it ~~here~~ *there* `N8` in the newspaper for myself. I asked him how well the exit polls from the last election ~~predict~~ *had predicted* `N5` the winner. He said they hadn't been accurate either! My daughter asked me what ~~was~~ *is/was* `N4` the purpose of exit polls. I didn't know, so I want to ask whether or not ~~should I~~ *I should* `N3` pay attention to them.

Sincerely,
Martha Smith

PART VIII Achievement Test

1 | LISTENING: ISSUES IN HIGHER EDUCATION

A.
1. say that it is important `U22`
2. What higher education refers to `U21`
3. whether to go `U21`
4. where to go `U21`
5. know that many jobs require `U22`
6. say that this is `U22`
7. claimed that cost was `U22`
8. where they studied `U21`
9. claimed that the tests don't measure `U22`
10. why universities also look `U21`

B.

Noun clause as a subject
The fact that higher education is valued so highly
what to study in college `U21`

Noun clause as an object
how much college costs
that standardized testing is another source of anxiety for students `U21`

2 | TUITION COSTS ON THE RISE

1. C `U22`
2. C `U22`
3. C `U22`
4. I `U22`
5. I `U22`
6. C `U22`
7. I `U22`
8. C `U22`

3 | TECHNICAL SCHOOLS AND UNIVERSITIES

1. me (that) he had decided to go `U22`
2. (that) I knew `U22`
3. (that) I didn't know `U22`
4. (that) a technical school trains `U22`
5. (that) the technical school sounded `U22`
6. (that) I was sure `U22`
7. (that) he hoped so `U22`
8. me (that) his father had gone `U22`
9. him (that) his father had been `U22`
10. if/whether (or not) that was because `U22`
11. (that) it had been `U22`
12. if/whether (or not) the school is/was `U22`
13. me (that) it is/was `U22`
14. if/whether (or not) I would let him `U22`
15. him (that) I would `U21`

4 | MAKING DECISIONS

1. what college she was planning `U22`
2. why she had chosen to go `U22`
3. how far Harvard was/is `U22`
4. how often she would visit home `U22`
5. where she would live `U22`
6. who her roommate would be `U21`
7. what she wanted to study `U21`
8. why she had decided `U21`
9. if/whether (or not) she would work `U22`
10. how she would pay `U21`
11. how many classes she could take `U21`
12. which classes she wanted to take `U21`
13. why she had chosen those `U21`
14. what other classes she would like `U21`

5 | EDITING: A LETTER HOME

Dear Mom and Dad,

    The first few weeks of the semester have been very busy. My classes are difficult, and how much I ~~X~~ study now is amazing. I didn't know how much

I would **U21**

~~would I~~ have to read! The other day, Alice asked

wanted **U21**

me if I ~~did want~~ to go to a movie, but I had a psychology test the next day, so I didn't go. I'm

by the fact that / that **U21**

worried ~~by that~~ I haven't gotten the graded test

we would **U21**

back yet. I asked the professor when ~~would we~~

told me / said **U22**

find out our grades. He ~~told~~ that he would give them to us soon.

I could **U21**

    Last time we talked, I asked you when ~~could I~~

whether / if **U21**

get a computer of my own. It's hard to know ∧a computer in the computer labs on campus will be

anything could **U21**

free or not. I don't know how ~~could anything~~ be more frustrating than when there aren't any

told me / said **U22**

computers available. Alice ~~said me~~ that having her own computer helps her get her work done more

That a **U21**

quickly. ~~A~~ laptop would be nice is obvious. Then I could take it to class with me to take notes! Do

that would be **U21**

you know how efficient ~~would that be~~? Just think about it, OK?

Love,
Kara

PART IX Diagnostic Test

1 | LISTENING: COMMON SENSE

A.

1. might **U23**
2. die **U23**
3. hadn't jumped **U23**
4. be able **U23**
5. don't pay **U23**
6. had thought **U23**
7. had used **U23**

B.

1. Otherwise, you will continue to have problems. **U24**
2. Had you thought about the consequences of your actions, those bad things would never have happened. **U24**

2 | IF ONLY . . .

1. b **U23**
2. d **U23**
3. a **U23**
4. d **U23**
5. a **U23**
6. c **U23**
7. a **U23**
8. b **U23**
9. d **U23**
10. c **U23**
11. a **U23**
12. d **U24**
13. b **U24**
14. c **U24**
15. b **U23**

3 | HEART ATTACK PREVENTION AND TREATMENT

1. desirable that you quit **U24**
2. insisting that their patients exercise **U24**
3. recommend getting 30 minutes of exercise **U24**
4. necessary that you maintain a healthy weight **U24**
5. recommending that their patients lose weight **U24**
6. important that you have a plan **U24**
7. essential that you know the number **U24**
8. crucial that you call for emergency medical treatment **U24**
9. recommend that you not wait longer than five minutes **U24**
10. desirable that you get help **U24**
11. suggest calling for help **U24**
12. ask that someone drive you **U24**
13. prefer that their patients prevent heart attacks **U24**
14. mandatory for hospital staff to give you emergency medical treatment **U24**

4 | LOST AND FOUND

Note: Both contracted forms and non-contracted forms are acceptable.

1. would not have happened **U23**
2. had known **U23**
3. do not see **U23**
4. did not do / were not doing **U23**
5. would be **U23**
6. not been **U24**
7. were **U23**
8. knew **U23**
9. would have made **U23**
10. would not have needed **U24**
11. had brought **U23**
12. would have stayed **U23**
13. had not made **U23**
14. flies **U23**

Dear Mom and Dad,

    I just arrived to my new home, and I'm

known

exhausted. Had I ~~know~~ that I would have so much trouble getting here, I would have done things differently. First of all, I put my passport in my pocket instead of in my bag, and I lost it! Dad, I

that I not keep / not keeping **U24**

know you recommended ~~me not to keep~~ it there,

Had I not / If I had not **U24**

but did I listen? No! ~~Had not I~~ put my passport in my pocket, I could have avoided a big mess. When I got off the plane, the immigration officer asked

show **U24**

that I ~~showed~~ him my passport. But I couldn't find it anywhere! I was so nervous because the officer

Had I not / If I had not **U24**

wouldn't let me through without it. ~~Hadn't I~~ lost my passport, I wouldn't have missed my connecting

had been **U24**

flight. Also, if I ~~were~~ thinking, I would have taken

Had I called / If I had called **U24**

my host family's number with me. ~~Were I to call~~ them, they wouldn't have gone to the airport to

would **U24**

get me. Were I to do it all over again, I ~~will~~ definitely be more careful.

Love,
Jen

Unit 23 Achievement Test

A.
1. know **N2**
2. paid **N3**
3. could find **N2**
4. will you find **N2**
5. had **N6a**
6. could be **N5**
7. had followed **N5**

B.
1. If only I had listened to my intuition! **N7**
2. (In that situation,) you could have gotten a better job if you had paid attention to your feelings. **N4**

1. a **N6a**
2. b **N6b**
3. c **N6c**
4. b **N6b**
5. b **N6c**

Note: Both contracted forms and non-contracted forms are acceptable.

1. could/would/might do **N3**
2. would/could/might change **N3**
3. had **N3**
4. will not come/do not come **N2**
5. will want/want **N2**
6. work **N2**
7. follow **N2**
8. would not have started **N4**
9. did not think/were not thinking **N4**
10. were not **N7**
11. had **N7**

MIKE: So, would you be really excited if you

got

~~would get~~ that job in Washington?

JOSH: Yeah, I would love that job, but I haven't heard from them. I shouldn't have waited so long to send in the forms. I might have heard

had **N4**

from them by now if I ₌applied earlier.

are you going to do / will you do **N2**

MIKE: What ~~are you doing~~ if you don't find a job before graduation?

don't **N2**

JOSH: If I ~~won't~~ get a job, I'll have to move back home for a while. I'd be so much less stressed

knew **N3**

right now if I ~~know~~ that I was going to get a job soon!

Unit 24 Achievement Test

A.
1. suggested **N5**
2. helping **N5**
3. start **N5**
4. do **N5**
5. doing **N5**
6. be paid **N3**
7. I were **N4**
8. not demand **N4**

B.
1. With such a plan, you'll start getting your money back immediately. **N1**
2. Otherwise, he might not listen to you at all. **N1**

1. ask **N6**
2. talk **N6**
3. explain **N6**
4. stay **N6**
5. work **N6**
6. behave **N6**
7. pay **N6**
8. sign **N6**

3 | BEST ACTOR

Note: Both contracted forms and non-contracted forms are acceptable.

1. if I were better prepared **N2**
2. If it were not for him/If it had not been for him **N1**
3. If it were not for him/If it had not been for him /If he had not been the director **N1**
4. If he should win/If he wins **N2**
5. If he has a little luck **N1**
6. If you win 30 more (awards) **N1**
7. If it were not for him **N2**
8. If they don't (have an award for you later tonight) **N1**
9. If you had not supported me **N2**

4 | EDITING: CARPET CLEANING

JIM: Hi, Honey. Why is the couch in the kitchen?
DIANE: I spilled juice on the carpet this morning, so I called the carpet cleaners and asked
that someone ~~came~~ *come* right away. The guy
recommended that I ~~moved~~ *move* **N4** the couch before
he got here, so I had to move it all by myself.
JIM: I'm sorry. I would have helped you if I ~~were~~ *had been* **N3**
home.
DIANE: That's okay. So he cleaned the carpet, but
he suggested ~~us to stay~~ *that we stay / staying* **N5** off it until tomorrow
morning.

PART IX Achievement Test

1 | LISTENING: STUDENT PROBLEMS

A.

1. would be **U23**
2. don't make **U23**
3. had studied **U23**
4. wouldn't have to **U23**
5. don't work **U23**
6. had followed **U23**
7. had known **U23**

B.

1. Otherwise, you might be unhappy for the rest of your life! **U24**
2. Had I known, I would have tried to help. **U24**

2 | TWENTY YEARS LATER

1. b **U23**
2. c **U23**
3. c **U23**
4. c **U23**
5. a **U23**
6. a **U23**
7. d **U23**
8. b **U23**
9. d **U23**
10. b **U23**
11. a **U23**
12. d **U24**
13. b **U24**
14. d **U24**
15. a **U23**

3 | AVOIDING AND PREPARING FOR FIRES

1. important that you have an evacuation plan **U24**
2. suggest that you have a fire drill **U24**
3. necessary that you leave a burning building **U24**
4. ask that a neighbor call for you **U24**
5. essential that you stay low to the floor **U24**
6. insists that local businesses identify multiple exits **U24**
7. crucial that you have smoke detectors **U24**
8. mandatory that landlords provide working smoke detectors **U24**
9. important that you keep a fire extinguisher **U24**
10. insisting that their upper-floor windows be equipped with escape ladders **U24**
11. recommend checking electrical outlets **U24**
12. desirable that you never smoke in bed **U24**
13. recommend that you not smoke in the house **U24**
14. prefer that you have updated information **U24**

4 | RUNNING OUT OF GAS

Note: Both contracted forms and non-contracted forms are acceptable.

1. would not have been **U23**
2. would not have forgotten **U23**
3. had not picked **U23**
4. would send **U23**
5. would not have gotten **U24**
6. were **U23**
7. would have arrived **U23**
8. would not have needed **U24**
9. had learned **U23**
10. would not have wasted **U23**
11. had not made **U23**
12. will remember **U23**
13. is **U23**
14. ran **U23**

Dear Kara,

    I just got home, and I'm exhausted. Had I

known

~~know~~ that I was going to have such a bad day, I would have stayed in bed. First of all, I forgot to fill up my car with gas last night, so I ran out of gas this morning on the way to work! I was hurrying because I had to give a presentation.

Had I not / If I had not **U24**

~~Had not I~~ been in such a hurry, I would have stopped to get gas. When I finally arrived at work

speak **U24**

half an hour late, my manager asked that I ~~spoke~~ to him. He said it was too late to give my

Had I not / If I had not **U24**

presentation. ~~Hadn't I~~ been late, I would have

that I write / writing **U24**

been able to give it. He recommended ~~me to write~~

had been **U24**

a formal apology to my colleagues. Also, if I ~~were~~ thinking, I would have learned my work number a

Had I called / If I had called **U24**

long time ago. ~~Were I to call~~ the office, my colleagues wouldn't have had to waste half an hour waiting for me. Were I to start the day over

would **U24**

again, I ~~will~~ definitely be more careful.

Love,
Eric

ETS Grammar Proficiency Tests

General Information

This section of the *Focus on Grammar 5 Assessment Pack* includes two Grammar Proficiency Tests (Form A and Form B) that were developed by Educational Testing Service (ETS). Each test includes 40 questions and takes 25 minutes. The tests were originally developed and administered by ETS as part of TOEFL®.

Because ETS has extensive data about the range of grammar proficiency of academic English learners, these tests can be used as independent benchmarks of students' general grammar proficiency. That is, students' scores on these tests indicate how their knowledge of English grammar compares with that of other academic English learners. The tests should *not* be used to draw any conclusions about students' performance on actual TOEFL exams.

ETS has determined the statistical difficulty of each test question by counting the number of TOEFL test-takers who answered the question correctly. A question that nearly everyone answers correctly is considered "easy"; one that only 65 or 70 percent of the population answers correctly is, relatively, "difficult." (If it seems illogical to call an item "difficult" when 70 percent of the test-takers answered correctly, remember that in a 4-choice question, 25 percent of the people who guess at random will select the correct answer.) Form A and Form B include items of the same general difficulty level, so the overall difficulty of Form A is the same as the overall difficulty of Form B. This means that you can expect students to receive the same (or a similar) score regardless of which form they use on a particular testing day. Over time, students' scores on these tests should improve as their knowledge of English grammar increases.

The two ETS Grammar Proficiency tests can be administered to students at any point during their course of study, and in any order, depending on how you want to use the test results. They can be used for a variety of purposes:

Purpose	When to Administer
1. to identify students who may need more support during the course of instruction	• Form A: before students begin their course • Form B: halfway through the course
2. to give students an idea of how their knowledge of English grammar compares to that of the TOEFL population (see "Scoring the Tests" below for further explanation)	• Form A: before students begin their course OR halfway through the course • Form B: after students have completed their course
3. to provide a measure of students' progress in their general grammar proficiency	• Form A: before students begin their course • Form B: after students have completed their course

Administering the Tests

Before administering each test, let students know that they will have 25 minutes to complete it. Hand out copies of the test and ask students to write their names at the top. Go over the directions and examples for both sections of the test, and ask students if they have any questions before they begin. Then start the time and tell students to begin.

After 20 minutes, let students know they have 5 minutes to complete the test. After 25 minutes, ask students to stop working and collect the tests.

Scoring the Tests

Use the Answer Key on page 240 to add up the number of questions the student answered correctly. This number is the student's raw score. To calculate the student's TOEFL percentile ranking, use the Score Conversion Charts on the next page.

For example, if a student answers 34 questions correctly on Form A, that student's percentile ranking is 77. This means that the student's score is higher than 77 percent of the students who have taken the Structure and Written Expression section of the TOEFL.

When you give students their test scores, tell them that these scores reflect their *general grammar proficiency* in comparison with other academic English language learners, not their knowledge of the specific content taught in *Focus on Grammar 5*.

Score Conversion Charts

The following tables are for informational purposes only.

Form A

RAW SCORE	PERCENTILE RANK
37–38	99
36	96
35	88
34	77
32–33	64
30–31	51
27–29	38
25–26	28
23–24	19
20–22	13
18–19	8
16–17	5
14–15	3
13	2
12	1
<12*	0*

Form B

RAW SCORE	PERCENTILE RANK
37–38	99
36	96
35	88
33–34	77
31–32	64
29–30	51
27–28	38
25–26	28
22–24	19
20–21	13
18–19	8
16–17	5
14–15	3
12–13	2
11	1
<11*	0*

* NOTE: Because the items on the ETS Grammar Proficiency Tests are multiple choice, most students will answer at least 11–12 items correctly, even if they are guessing.

ETS Grammar Proficiency Test

Form A

This test is designed to measure your ability to recognize language that is appropriate for standard written English. There are two types of questions on this test, with special directions for each type.

PART 1

Directions: *Questions 1–15 are incomplete sentences. Beneath each sentence you will see four words or phrases, marked (A), (B), (C), and (D). Circle the letter of the ONE word or phrase that best completes the sentence.*

Example I

Geysers have often been compared to volcanoes _____ they both emit hot liquids from below the Earth's surface.

A Ⓑ C D

(**A**) due to
(**B**) because

(**C**) in spite of
(**D**) regardless of

The sentence should read, "Geysers have often been compared to volcanoes because they both emit hot liquids from below the Earth's surface." Therefore, you should choose (**B**).

Example II

During the early period of ocean navigation, _____ any need for sophisticated instruments and techniques.

A B C Ⓓ

(**A**) so that hardly
(**B**) when there hardly was

(**C**) hardly was
(**D**) there was hardly

The sentence should read, "During the early period of ocean navigation, there was hardly any need for sophisticated instruments and techniques." Therefore, you should choose (**D**).

Now begin work on the questions.

Go on to the next page ➡

1. While learning their native language, children must make up,   **A B C D**
without being fully aware _____, provisional sets of rules
for what is grammatical and what is not.

     (**A**) that it   (**C**) it
     (**B**) of it   (**D**) it is

2. _____ everywhere in ocean waters, which cover 70   **A B C D**
percent of the Earth's surface.

     (**A**) Animals live   (**C**) The life of animals
     (**B**) Animals living   (**D**) Animals to live

3. _____ relationship between an actor and the character   **A B C D**
portrayed is central to the success of a theatrical presentation.

     (**A**) Whatever the   (**C**) Because the
     (**B**) It is the   (**D**) The

4. On the west bank of the Connecticut River, about halfway   **A B C D**
between Boston and New York City, _____.

     (**A**) lies the city of Hartford   (**C**) the city of Hartford it lies there
     (**B**) where does the city of Hartford lie   (**D**) lies where the city of Hartford

5. The biggest difference between business and politics lies not   **A B C D**
in the multiplicity of interests _____ in the relationship
between money and power.

     (**A**) despite   (**C**) while
     (**B**) though   (**D**) but

6. Within the brain _____ chemicals called neurotransmitters,   **A B C D**
which transfer signals from one brain cell to another.

     (**A**) there are   (**C**) the
     (**B**) where   (**D**) there

7. Margaret Mary Heckler served as Secretary of Health and   **A B C D**
Human Services from 1983 to 1985, _____ by President
Ronald Reagan.

     (**A**) a position to which she was appointed   (**C**) appointing her to the position
     (**B**) a position she appointed   (**D**) the appointment of her to this position

8. On the coast of the Pacific Northwest of the United States, an   **A B C D**
annual rainfall of _____ 150 inches is possible.

     (**A**) so much   (**C**) much more
     (**B**) as much as   (**D**) so much that

Go on to the next page ➡

9. In 1609 Henry Hudson explored the river _____ bears his name.   **A B C D**

   (**A**) that now it   (**C**) that now
   (**B**) now   (**D**) to now

10. The most productive fields of California's Central Valley _____ the city of Fresno.   **A B C D**

    (**A**) around   (**C**) which is around
    (**B**) around those   (**D**) are those around

11. _____ a machine can never do more work than the energy put into it is true.   **A B C D**

    (**A**) Which   (**C**) That
    (**B**) How   (**D**) If

12. _____ constructed in patterns of rhythmic repetition, but it also consists of interlocking word sounds.   **A B C D**

    (**A**) Poetry, being not only   (**C**) Not only is poetry
    (**B**) Is poetry not only   (**D**) Poetry, which is not only

13. Earthquakes occur in the Earth's crust _____ they generate travel far and deep into the Earth.   **A B C D**

    (**A**) waves   (**C**) and of the waves
    (**B**) while the waves   (**D**) because of the waves

14. The Hartford Wits, a group of eighteenth-century poets, advocated a revision of Yale University's curriculum _____ the literature of the United States.   **A B C D**

    (**A**) included   (**C**) to include
    (**B**) was including   (**D**) the inclusion of

15. Algebra is _____ that is used in virtually every area of natural science.   **A B C D**

    (**A**) a branch of mathematics   (**C**) of a branch is mathematics
    (**B**) a branch that mathematics   (**D**) what branch of mathematics

Go on to the next page ➤

PART 2

Directions: *In questions 16–40 each sentence has four underlined words or phrases. The four underlined parts of the sentence are marked (A), (B), (C), and (D). Circle the letter of the ONE underlined word or phrase that must be changed in order for the sentence to be correct.*

Example I

Guppies are sometimes <u>call</u> rainbow <u>fish</u> <u>because of</u> the   Ⓐ **B C D**
              A   **B**   **C**

males' <u>bright</u> colors.
    D

The sentence should read, "Guppies are sometimes called rainbow fish because of the males' bright colors." Therefore, you should choose (**A**).

Example II

<u>Serving</u> several <u>term</u> in Congress, Shirley Chisholm became   **A** Ⓑ **C D**
 A   **B**

an <u>important</u> figure in United States <u>politics</u>.
      C   **D**

The sentence should read, "Serving several terms in Congress, Shirley Chisholm became an important figure in United States politics." Therefore, you should choose (**B**).

Now begin work on the questions.

Go on to the next page ➤

16. Most apples are <u>ate</u> raw, <u>but they</u> are <u>also</u> used <u>in</u> jellies, **A B C D**

       A   **B**   **C**   **D**

    pies, puddings, and applesauce.

17. James Buchanan, <u>the</u> fifteenth president of the United States, **A B C D**

           A

    <u>served</u> his country <u>as a</u> congressman, senator,

B   **C**

    <u>ambassadorial</u>, and secretary of state.

   D

18. <u>The rise</u> of modern, large-scale dairy farming was stimulated **A B C D**

   A

    <u>by</u> the invention <u>of</u> the cream separator and <u>another</u>

B   **C**   **D**

    specialized machines.

19. Anne Dudley Bradstreet, born in England about 1612, moved **A B C D**

    to North America <u>as young</u> woman <u>and</u> became one of <u>the</u>

           A   **B**   **C**

    first poets to publish works <u>there</u>.

             D

20. Companies <u>must</u> restructure their personnel policies so that <u>it</u> **A B C D**

         A   **B**

    will use the skills <u>already found</u> in the work force <u>more</u>

          C   **D**

    efficiently.

21. Canals <u>enable</u> barges, <u>boating</u>, and ships <u>to carry</u> goods **A B C D**

      A   **B**   **C**

    <u>from</u> river to river, between rivers and lakes, and between

D

    oceans and lakes.

22. An <u>arrangement</u> between two species <u>in what</u> each benefits **A B C D**

     A   **B**

    <u>from</u> the other and neither <u>is harmed</u> by the relationship is

C   **D**

    called mutualism.

23. The mineral jasper is <u>harder</u> <u>than</u> than the blade of a knife **A B C D**

          A   **B**

    <u>and</u> will even <u>scratches</u> glass.

C   **D**

Go on to the next page ➡

24. During <u>the</u> late 1800's, the botanist Asa Gray <u>became</u> the
         A   **B**

    <u>authority leading</u> on the <u>plant life</u> of the United States.
        C   **D**

A B C D

25. All <u>people dream</u>, <u>whether</u> <u>they</u> want to or <u>not want</u>.
         A   **B** **C**   **D**

A B C D

26. Each <u>of</u> the <u>planet</u> in our Solar System revolves <u>around</u> the
      A   **B**   **C**

    Sun <u>in an</u> elliptical orbit.
        D

A B C D

27. Bebop is a jazz style, <u>characterized by</u> fast tempos and <u>highly</u>
                   A   **B**

    syncopated rhythms, developed <u>at</u> the decade after the
                             C

    Second World War by <u>small groups</u> of musicians.
                    D

A B C D

28. Impressionist painters <u>were</u> mainly concerned with <u>how</u> the
                     A   **B**

    surfaces of <u>object</u> appeared to the eye at a <u>particular</u>
              C   **D**

    moment.

A B C D

29. <u>Though</u> hydrocarbons <u>are unaffecting</u> by ordinary reagents,
    A   **B**

    they all burn <u>in air</u> to <u>yield</u> carbon dioxide and water.
              C   **D**

A B C D

30. <u>During</u> the nineteenth century, most scientists came to
    A

    believe that everything <u>was made of</u> atoms, even though <u>it</u>
                     B   **C**

    had no way then <u>to observe</u> atoms.
              D

A B C D

31. Learning to <u>dealt with</u> stress <u>may provide</u> psychological
           A   **B**

    benefits and <u>relief from</u> physiological ailments as <u>well</u>.
             C   **D**

A B C D

32. <u>Inherent</u> in all philosophical methods is <u>an attempt</u> to think,
    A   **B**

    speak, and write <u>precise</u>.
    <u>speak</u>,
    C   **D**

A B C D

Go on to the next page

33. <u>Extending</u> in the human body <u>to</u> the brain to the <u>base</u> of the
        A   B   C

   torso, the spinal cord is the main highway for neurological

   <u>messages</u> to and from the brain.
      D

       A B C D

34. Capillaries interact <u>with</u> tissues throughout the body to deliver
                    A

   oxygen and nutrients and serve the <u>vital</u> function of <u>removal</u>
                                     B   C

   carbon dioxide and <u>other waste</u> products.
                     D

       A B C D

35. Volcanoes forming <u>beneath</u> the surface <u>at</u> the sea <u>rarely</u>
                      A   B   C

   cause <u>any damage</u> to property.
          D

       A B C D

36. An eloquent spokeswoman for the antislavery <u>movement</u>,
                                            A

   Sojourner Truth was among the <u>most notable</u> and <u>high</u>
                                  B   C

   regarded African American <u>women</u> in the nineteenth century.
                       D

       A B C D

37. Chi Chi Rodriguez <u>holds</u> corporate golf clinics, stages golf
                    A

   exhibitions, and gets <u>fellow</u> sports stars to help <u>raise money</u>
                   B   C

   for <u>children disadvantaged</u>.
           D

       A B C D

38. Vitamins <u>and</u> minerals will keep for <u>a long time</u> <u>if protected</u>
           A   B   C

   from light, <u>moist</u>, and heat.
           D

       A B C D

39. <u>When fish</u> breathes, it opens its mouth at <u>regular</u> intervals
       A   B

   and <u>draws</u> in a <u>mouthful</u> of water.
        C   D

       A B C D

40. The facsimile transmission of <u>documents</u>, diagrams, and
                               A

   photographs over a telephone network has been <u>wide</u>
                                       B

   available for <u>international</u> communication <u>since</u> 1986.
             C   D

       A B C D

ETS Grammar Proficiency Test

Form B

This test is designed to measure your ability to recognize language that is appropriate for standard written English. There are two types of questions on this test, with special directions for each type.

PART 1

Directions: *Questions 1–15 are incomplete sentences. Beneath each sentence you will see four words or phrases, marked (A), (B), (C), and (D). Circle the letter of the ONE word or phrase that best completes the sentence.*

Example I

Geysers have often been compared to volcanoes _____ they both emit hot liquids from below the Earth's surface.

A Ⓑ **C** **D**

(**A**) due to   (**C**) in spite of
(**B**) because   (**D**) regardless of

The sentence should read, "Geysers have often been compared to volcanoes because they both emit hot liquids from below the Earth's surface." Therefore, you should choose (**B**).

Example II

During the early period of ocean navigation, _____ any need for sophisticated instruments and techniques.

A **B** **C** Ⓓ

(**A**) so that hardly   (**C**) hardly was
(**B**) when there hardly was   (**D**) there was hardly

The sentence should read, "During the early period of ocean navigation, there was hardly any need for sophisticated instruments and techniques." Therefore, you should choose (**D**).

Now begin work on the questions.

Go on to the next page ▶

1. Telephone cables that use optical fibers can be _____ **A B C D**
   conventional cables, yet they typically carry much more
   information.

   (**A**) they are smaller and lighter   (**C**) smaller and lighter than
   (**B**) than the smaller and lighter   (**D**) so small and light that

2. In making cheese, _____, is coagulated by enzyme action, **A B C D**
   by lactic acid, or by both.

   (**A**) casein is the chief milk protein   (**C**) the chief milk protein is casein
   (**B**) casein, being that the chief milk protein (**D**) casein, the chief milk protein

3. Sensory structures _____ from the heads of some **A B C D**
   invertebrates are called antennae.

   (**A**) are growing   (**C**) that grow
   (**B**) they are growing   (**D**) grow

4. Because of an optical illusion, the Moon appears to be larger **A B C D**
   _____ close to the horizon.

   (**A**) when it is   (**C**) than is
   (**B**) it is as   (**D**) which is

5. Newspaper historians feel that Joseph Pulitzer exercised **A B C D**
   _____ on American journalism during his lifetime.

   (**A**) influence remarkable   (**C**) influence was remarkable
   (**B**) remarkable for his influence   (**D**) remarkable influence

6. As Secretary of Housing and Urban Development, Carla A. **A B C D**
   Hills worked _____ from the economic slump of the 1970's.

   (**A**) she helped America's housing industry recover
   (**B**) the recovery of America's housing industry helped
   (**C**) to help America's housing industry recover
   (**D**) for the recovery of America's housing industry to help

7. The safflower plant is grown chiefly for the oil _____ from **A B C D**
   its seeds.

   (**A**) obtained   (**C**) which obtains it
   (**B**) is obtaining   (**D**) obtaining that

8. _____ late July and early August that the Earth rotates at **A B C D**
   its greatest speed.

   (**A**) There is in   (**C**) In it
   (**B**) It is in   (**D**) In

Go on to the next page ➡

9. In 1984 Kathryn Sullivan became the first female astronaut _____ in space.   A B C D

    (**A**) would walk   (**C**) was walking
    (**B**) walked   (**D**) to walk

10. _____ must have water to lay and fertilize their eggs, whereas their offspring, tadpoles, need water for development and growth.   A B C D

    (**A**) Though frogs and toads   (**C**) That frogs and toads
    (**B**) Frogs and toads   (**D**) If frogs and toads

11. In 1964 the United States Bureau of the Census estimated that California had become the most populous state, _____ New York.   A B C D

    (**A**) surpasses   (**C**) surpassed
    (**B**) surpassing   (**D**) had surpassed

12. _____ not for its addictive properties, morphine would be used more frequently to relieve pain.   A B C D
    (**A**) If it   (**C**) Were it
    (**B**) It is   (**D**) Why

13. The American philosopher and educator John Dewey rejected _____.   A B C D

    (**A**) to use authoritarian teaching methods   (**C**) for authoritarian teaching methods
    (**B**) that authoritarian teaching methods   (**D**) authoritarian teaching methods

14. _____ can be partially credited to the cooperation of Canadian politicians Robert Baldwin and Louis H. Lafontaine, who fought for responsible government during the 1840's.   A B C D

    (**A**) Today a member of the Commonwealth, Canada
    (**B**) That Canada is today a member of the Commonwealth
    (**C**) Today, Canada is a member of the Commonwealth
    (**D**) It is Canada, as a member of the Commonwealth

15. _____ many food preservation methods for inhibiting the growth of bacteria.   A B C D

    (**A**) The   (**C**) There are
    (**B**) Because   (**D**) Having

Go on to the next page ➤

PART 2

Directions: *In questions 16–40 each sentence has four underlined words or phrases. The four underlined parts of the sentence are marked (A), (B), (C), and (D). Circle the letter of the ONE underlined word or phrase that must be changed in order for the sentence to be correct.*

Example I

Guppies are sometimes <u>call</u> rainbow <u>fish</u> <u>because of</u> the
             A   **B**   **C**

males' <u>bright</u> colors.
     D

Ⓐ **B C D**

The sentence should read, "Guppies are sometimes called rainbow fish because of the males' bright colors." Therefore, you should choose (**A**).

Example II

<u>Serving</u> several <u>term</u> in Congress, Shirley Chisholm became
  A   **B**

an <u>important</u> figure in United States <u>politics</u>.
    C   **C**

A Ⓑ **C D**

The sentence should read, "Serving several terms in Congress, Shirley Chisholm became an important figure in United States politics." Therefore, you should choose (**B**).

Now begin work on the questions.

Go on to the next page ➤

16. One of the United States' <u>most</u> renowned <u>painters</u>, Grandma
                A   **B**

    Moses was in her seventies when <u>her</u> began to paint <u>seriously</u>.
                              C   **D**

    A B C D

17. The novelty, relatively high speed, and <u>advantageously</u> of
                                  A

    year-round service <u>made</u> early <u>passenger</u> <u>trains</u> a popular
                  B   **C**   **D**

    form of transportation.

    A B C D

18. Statistical evidence <u>indicates that</u> the century-old trend in the
                         A

    United States of children <u>are</u> taller than their parents <u>seems</u>
                       B   **C**

    to have <u>leveled off</u>.
           D

    A B C D

19. Many artists use watercolors on <u>outdoor</u> sketching <u>trips</u>
                         A   **B**

    because the <u>equipment</u> is light, compact, and easily
             C

    <u>transport</u>.
    D

    A B C D

20. Basketball <u>is</u> one of the leading <u>sport</u> in the United States,
          A   **B**

    <u>attracting</u> well over thirty million spectators <u>every</u> year.
    C   **D**

    A B C D

21. <u>Because incomplete</u> records, the <u>number of enlistments</u> in the
    A   **B**

    Confederate army <u>has long been</u> <u>in dispute</u>.
                 C   **D**

    A B C D

22. The <u>power</u> of Gwendolyn Brooks' poetry often results from
      A

    her innovative style, her <u>elegant</u> lyricism, and her <u>combine</u> of
                    B   **C**

    formal language with informal <u>speech</u>.
                     D

    A B C D

23. Musical instruments are <u>divided into</u> various types, depending
                    A

    <u>on whether</u> the vibration that produces <u>their sound</u> is made
    B   **C**

    by striking, scraping, or <u>is blown</u>.
                  D

    A B C D

24. The Federal Theater Project, the first federally <u>financed</u>
                          A

    theater project in the United States, <u>was</u> established <u>to</u>
                       B   **C**

    <u>benefit</u> theater personnel <u>while</u> the Depression of the 1930's.
    D

    A B C D

Go on to the next page ➡

25. Estuaries are <u>highly</u> sensitive and ecologically <u>important</u>   **A B C D**
    　　　　　　　　A   B

    habitats, <u>providing</u> breeding and feeding grounds for <u>much</u>
    　　　　　　C   D

    life-forms.

26. As <u>early the</u> seventeenth century <u>various</u> North American   **A B C D**
    　　　A   B

    colonies enacted construction <u>regulations</u> for buildings <u>to help</u>
    　　　　　　　　　　　　　　　　　C   D

    prevent the spread of fires.

27. <u>When</u> the thermometer drops <u>below</u> 68 degrees Fahrenheit,   **A B C D**
    　A   B

    the body conserves <u>warm</u> by <u>restricting</u> blood flowing to the
    　　　　　　　　　　　C   D

    skin.

28. Although best known <u>for great</u> novel *The Grapes of Wrath*,   **A B C D**
    　　　　　　　　　　　　A

    John Steinbeck <u>also</u> published essays, <u>plays</u>, stories,
    　　　　　　　　　B   C

    memoirs, and newspaper <u>articles</u>.
    　　　　　　　　　　　　　　D

29. Carl Sagan, the <u>renowned</u> astronomer, served <u>as</u> an <u>advice</u> to   **A B C D**
    　　　　　　　　　A   B   C

    NASA and <u>to</u> the National Academy of Sciences.
    　　　　　　D

30. <u>Few</u> jurists have left <u>too deep</u> an imprint <u>on</u> the law and   **A B C D**
    　A   B   C

    government of <u>their</u> country as John Marshall.
    　　　　　　　　D

31. A cicada is a <u>big</u> insect with a wide <u>head</u>, large protruding <u>the</u>   **A B C D**
    　　　　　　　　A   B   C

    eyes, and two <u>pairs of wings</u>.
    　　　　　　　　D

32. The contralto is <u>the lowest</u> female singing <u>voice</u>, with a <u>range</u>   **A B C D**
    　　　　　　　　　A   B   C

    of about two <u>and half</u> octaves upward from about E in the
    　　　　　　　　D

    bass clef.

33. <u>Sponges live</u> in colonies <u>attached the</u> ocean floor <u>or</u> <u>other</u>   **A B C D**
    　A   B   C   D

    surfaces.

Go on to the next page ➤

34. The <u>vivid</u> <u>markings</u> of the leopard's fur make it <u>value</u> as a zoo
     A   **B**   **C**

   <u>attraction</u>.
    D

                         A B C D

35. <u>The most</u> mammals have two sets of teeth <u>during</u> their
     A   **B**

   lifetime, <u>consisting of</u> the temporary teeth and the permanent
          C

   <u>ones</u>.
   D

                         A B C D

36. The political and economic life of the <u>state</u> of Rhode Island
                        A

   <u>was dominated</u> by the owners of textile mills <u>well</u> into the
      B   **C**

   <u>twenty</u> century.
   D

                         A B C D

37. Deriving <u>its</u> energy from <u>warm</u> tropical ocean water,
       A   **B**

   hurricanes weaken after <u>prolonged</u> contact with colder
                 C

   <u>northern</u> ocean waters.
   D

                         A B C D

38. Lichens <u>grow</u> in a variety of places, <u>ranging</u> from dry <u>area</u> to
       A   **B**   **C**

   moist rainforests, to freshwater lakes, and even <u>to</u> bodies of
                           D

   salt water.

                         A B C D

39. <u>Some of</u> playwrights <u>provide</u> extensive instructions in the
    A   **B**

   text of their plays on <u>how</u> the plays should be <u>interpreted by</u>
               C   **D**

   actors and directors.

                         A B C D

40. After launching the Hubble Space Telescope into orbit, <u>a</u>
                           A

   makers <u>discovered</u> <u>that</u> its original main mirror had a <u>major</u>
          B   **C**   **D**

   flaw that subsequently had to be repaired.

Answer Key

Form A

1. B	11. C	21. B	31. A
2. A	12. C	22. B	32. D
3. D	13. B	23. D	33. B
4. A	14. C	24. C	34. C
5. D	15. A	25. D	35. B
6. A	16. A	26. B	36. C
7. A	17. D	27. C	37. D
8. B	18. D	28. C	38. D
9. C	19. A	29. B	39. A
10. D	20. B	30. C	40. B

Form B

1. C	11. B	21. A	31. C
2. D	12. C	22. C	32. D
3. C	13. D	23. D	33. B
4. A	14. B	24. D	34. C
5. D	15. C	25. D	35. A
6. C	16. C	26. A	36. D
7. A	17. A	27. C	37. A
8. B	18. B	28. A	38. C
9. D	19. D	29. C	39. A
10. B	20. B	30. B	40. A

Test Generating CD-ROM

General Information

The test generating CD-ROM (TestGen®) that accompanies the *Focus on Grammar Assessment Pack* provides you with the TestGen software program and a testbank of hundreds of items per level. You can use the software program to create and customize tests. With TestGen, you can:

- create tests quickly using the TestGen Wizard
- select questions by part, unit, or grammar topic
- edit questions
- add your own questions
- create multiple versions of a test

Because the items in the TestGen testbank are different from those in the printed tests, you can use TestGen to create additional tests, review quizzes, or practice exercises.

Organization of Items in the *Focus on Grammar* TestGen CD-ROM

The *Focus on Grammar* TestGen CD-ROM includes five testbanks, one for each level of *Focus on Grammar*. Within each testbank, the items are divided by part of the Student Book.

Each *Focus on Grammar* test item is labeled for easy sorting. You can sort by grammar point or unit. See "How to Create a Test" for an example of a test with items sorted by grammar point.

How to Create a Test

There are two ways to create a test using the TestGen software. You can create a test manually, or you can use the TestGen Wizard.

Using the TestGen Wizard to Create a Test The TestGen Wizard is the easiest, fastest way to create a customized test. Follow these easy steps to create a test.

STEP 1
Select a **Testbank** from the **Testbank Library** window.

STEP 2
Click on **Use the TestGen Wizard to create a new paper test** icon.

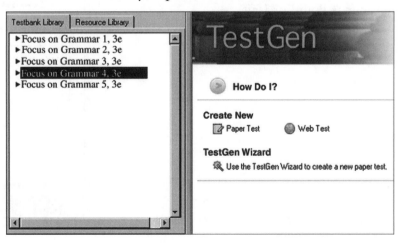

STEP 3
When the **TestGen Wizard** launches, you will be prompted to enter a name for your test. After assigning a name to your test, click the **Next** button to proceed.

STEP 4
Select the part or parts you want to include in your test.

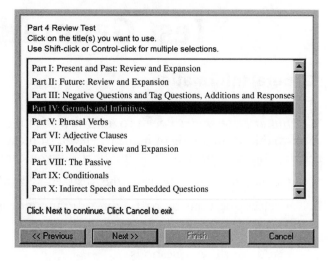

STEP 5
On the next screen, you will choose "Select questions randomly" or "Select specific questions from a list." Choose **Select questions randomly** and click the **Next** button.

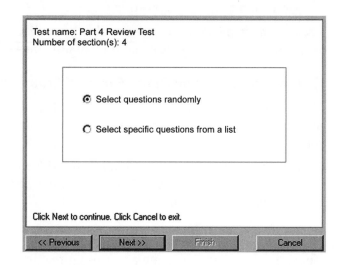

STEP 6
Use the drop-down list to choose questions randomly by Question Type, Section,* Grammar Point, or Unit.

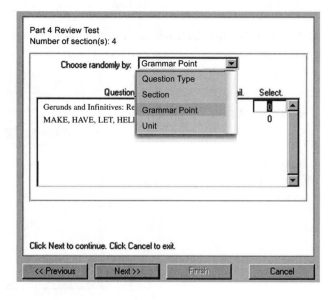

---

* "Section" refers to *Focus on Grammar* parts. Each level has 8 to 10 parts.

STEP 7

Under the "Select" column, choose the number of items you want in the test. Click the **Next** button to continue to the **Test Summary.**

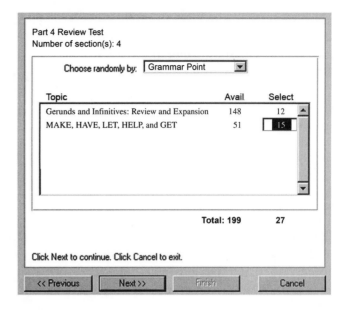

STEP 8

The **Test Summary** window will display the name of your test, the number of sections (parts) you selected, the selection method, and the total number of questions on the test. Click **Finish** to build the test.

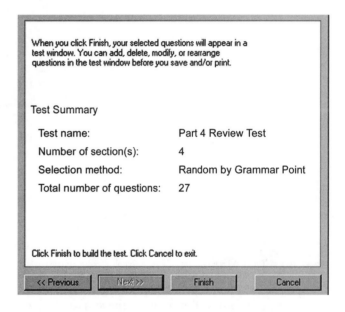

STEP 9

The **TestGen Wizard** will close, and a **Test Window** will open with your selected questions.

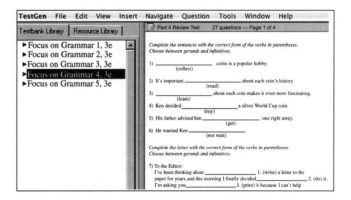

STEP 10

To put your questions in the correct order, click on the **Question** menu at the top of the screen and select **Sort**.

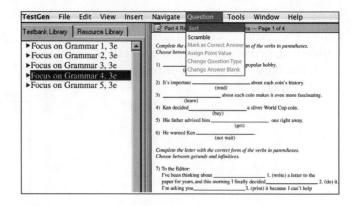

STEP 11

Next, click **Keep questions in the same order as they are in the testbank** under **SmartSort by test bank order** and click **OK.**

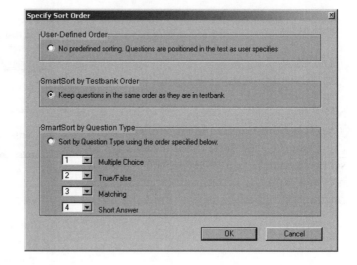

STEP 12

Finish by saving and/or printing the test.

Creating a Test Manually To create a test manually:

1. Open the TestGen software and select a **Testbank** from the **Testbank Library** window.
2. Click on the **Paper Test** icon in the startup pane. A new blank test appears.
3. Click on the arrows in the **Testbank Library** window to expand the outline and see the testbank questions.
4. Drag and drop each question you want to include into the **Test** window.

For more information, see the User's Guide located on the TestGen CD-ROM in the "Resources" folder.

How to Create New Questions

To add a new question to your test:

1. Click the place in the **Test window** where you want to add a new question.
2. In the menu bar, click **Insert > Question.**
3. Choose a **Question Type** from the drop down menu.
4. Double-click on the new question in the **Test** window.
5. Type the question and answer into the appropriate fields.

How to Edit Questions

To edit a question in your test:

1. Click on the **Tools** menu at the top of the screen and select **Preferences > Test Options**.
2. Click on the **Descriptors** tab.
3. Check **Correct Answer** to display the answers in the Test window.
4. Return to the test window and double-click on the question you want to edit.
5. Make any changes you want to both the question and answer.

How to Change the Order of Questions

If you want to move a question to a specific location in the test:

1. Click on the **Tools** menu and select **Sort**.
2. Click **User-defined order.**
3. Click **OK.**
4. Now you can drag the question to any location you want in the test.

Other TestGen Features

You can modify your TestGen test in many ways. You can change the display, create questions with graphics, edit direction lines, and much, much more. To learn more about the features that the TestGen software offers, go to the *Focus on Grammar* Companion Website (www.longman.com/focusongrammar) and click on the TestGen link.

TestGen 7.2 System Requirements

Windows®

Operating System:	Microsoft® Windows NT®, Windows 2000 or Windows XP	
Processor	233MHz or faster Pentium-compatible processor	
Random access memory (RAM)	128 MB	
Available hard disk space	20 MB (varies depending on testbank size)	
Web browser*	Windows NT®	Internet Explorer 5.5 or Netscape® Navigator 6.2.3
	Windows 2000	Internet Explorer 5.5, 6.0 or Netscape Navigator 6.2.3
	Windows XP	Internet Explorer 6.0 or Netscape Navigator 7.0

Macintosh®

Operating System:	Mac OS X v 10.2, 10.3, 10.4**
Processor	PowerPC G3, G4, or G5 processor
Random access memory (RAM)	128 MB
Available hard disk space	20 MB (varies depending on testbank size)
Web browser*	Internet Explorer 5.2 or Netscape Navigator 7.0

*Required only for viewing TestGen tests on the Web with TestGen Plug-in and for viewing TestGen Help.

**The TestGen application is supported on Mac OS X v 10.3 and 10.4. The TestGen Plug-in is not currently supported on this platform.

Installing TestGen

Windows Computers

- Insert the TestGen CD into your computer's CD drive.

- Open **My Computer**. Then double click on the CD drive icon.

- Double-click on "tgesetup.exe."

- Follow the directions on the screen to complete the installation. Once the installation is complete the program will begin automatically.

Macintosh Computers

- Insert the TestGen CD into your computer's CD drive.

- Double-click on "TestGen 7 Setup."

- Follow the directions on the screen to complete the installation. Once the installation is complete the program will begin automatically.

Note:

If you have existing versions of TestGen on your computer, you will receive a message providing you with the option to remove earlier versions of the program. Click *Yes* to remove the older TestGen versions and continue (recommended).

Removing older versions of the TestGen program does not delete or otherwise compromise tests and testbanks created with earlier versions of the program located on your computer. You can convert older tests and testbanks simply by opening them in the TestGen 7.2 program.

Product Support

The *User's Guide* can be found on the TestGen CD in the "Resources" folder (see TG7UserGuide.pdf). It provides detailed instructions about how to use all of TestGen's tools and features. Once TestGen has been installed, the *User's Guide* is also available by clicking "Help" in the TestGen menu at the top of the screen. To view the *User's Guide,* Adobe® Acrobat® Reader® is required. This free software can be installed from the Internet at the following address: www.adobe.com/acrobat.

For further technical assistance:

- Call Pearson's toll-free product support line: 1-800-677-6337

- Send an email to media.support@pearsoned.com

- Fill out a web form at: http://247.pearsoned.com/mediaform

Our technical staff will need to know certain things about your system in order to help us solve your problems more quickly and efficiently. If possible, please be at your computer when you call for support. You should have the following information ready:

- Product title and product ISBN

- Computer make and model

- RAM available

- Hard disk space available

- Graphics card type

- Printer make and model (if applicable)

- Detailed description of the problem, including the exact wording of any error messages.